GARDEN LIFE

GARDEN LIFE

Jennifer Owen

CHATTO & WINDUS
THE HOGARTH PRESS
LONDON

First published in 1983 by
Chatto & Windus/The Hogarth Press
40 William IV Street
London WC2N 4DF

Clarke, Irwin & Co Ltd
Toronto

BRITISH LIBRARY
CATALOGUING IN PUBLICATION DATA

Owen, Jennifer
Garden life.
1. Garden fauna—England—Leicester
2. Seasons—England—Leicester
I. Title
574.5'43'0924   QH138.L/
ISBN-0-7011-2610-8

Photoset in Great Britain by
Rowland Phototypesetting Ltd
Bury St Edmunds, Suffolk
and printed by
Redwood Burn Ltd
Trowbridge, Wiltshire

Contents

List of illustrations

Acknowledgements

Many people have contributed to my knowledge and understanding of life in my garden. Some have identified animals for me; others have helped in discussion or correspondence, or through their published work. Gardening and garden-watching are joint ventures with Denis Owen, who made constructive comments on an earlier draft of this book. I am particularly indebted to him, and to Michael Archer, Alan Bak, R. R. Baker, Maureen and Bridget Boland, W. S. Bristowe, Philip S. Callahan, James Dear, J. P. Dempster, A. F. G. Dixon, John H. Falk, John B. Free and Colin G. Butler, Francis S. Gilbert, Don Goddard, Roy Hay, Ronald Hickling, Richard M. Jackson and Frank Raw, Geoffrey Kibby, G. F. Le Pard, Teresa McLean, R. K. Murton, Richard Owen, Stephen Potter and Laurens Sargent, Michael Proctor and Peter Yeo, David Snow, Stephen Sutton, J. O. Tahvanainen and Richard B. Root, Henry and Marjorie Townes, and Thomas G. Whitham.

Setting the scene

The garden image that I carry with me to warm and lighten the coldest and greyest winter days is the joy of raspberry-picking in early July. Mint grows all through the raspberry patch and, as I reach beneath the netting to pick ripe, red berries, its leaves get bruised, their rich aroma mingling with the delicate scent of the fruit. Spotted dead-nettle straggles beneath the canes, attracting ponderous white-tailed bumblebees, which can reach the nectar deep within the hooded, purple flowers. The splay-legged, black larvae of ladybirds lurk on the mint, growing fat on aphids infesting the new leaves. Other less conspicuous insects share the raspberry patch – and the berries: a minute, parasitic wasp runs to and fro over the raspberry leaves searching for a soft-bodied insect in which to lay its eggs; a tiny, flattened bug crawls from a freshly-picked berry; and a small, dingy caterpillar, dispossessed of its fruity home, wriggles astonishingly quickly across the bowl of fruit. Plump young blackbirds, frustrated in their repeated attempts to storm the netting, skulk close at hand, ready, should opportunity arise, to sneak a succulent mouthful, while nearby their somewhat worn father is diligently collecting worms and other food for his second or third brood of the year. The rhythmic lament of a collared dove perched on a chimney-pot is intermittently drowned by the brash screams of swifts – Jack-squealers, as they used to be known locally – hawking for insects in the sky above. This medley of sights, scents and sounds remains alive and fresh in mind and memory throughout the winter months when the raspberry canes are bare, the swifts are far away in Africa, and the garden is still and silent.

I cannot imagine living without a garden. It is an extension not just of the physical space of the house, but also of scope for interest and pleasure, providing elbow room for the mind as well as the body. Fruit, herbs, vegetables and flowers are the tangible rewards of gardening, but there is more to a garden than its produce: it provides opportunity to see, hear and smell the living world, to appreciate the changing seasons, and for me added delight lies in finding out what insects, birds and other animals live there, and in tracing their complex interactions with one another and with garden plants. Gardening is one of the most intensive forms of land management, and so, like it or not, every gardener participates in the lives of the animals and plants that share the garden. For me, the outcome of spending time and energy on digging, planting, pruning, weeding and other chores is a complex community of animals and plants which arouses curiosity, poses questions and prompts investigation. Every stroll around the garden leaves me with a query: who nibbled that leaf? where have all the ladybirds gone? what is that bee doing on the bare earth? why is that plant losing its leaves? To me this is the joy of having a garden – being able to satisfy curiosity and eventually to understand some of the intricacies of the living world.

This is not a conventional gardening book. I cannot tell you how to grow prize runner beans or perfect roses – others have plenty of advice on such matters. But I can show you what else there is to enjoy and wonder at in your own private plot, and share with you my enthusiasm for gardening with a difference.

How it all began

My father has green fingers, and I grew up accepting that gardening is an absorbing activity with much hard work and many rewards. But I also learnt that there is more to a garden than colourful displays of flowers, abundant garden produce, trim lawns and eye-catching shrubs, for my father participated in the bird-ringing scheme which has yielded such a wealth of information about migration, local movements and longevity of birds. A large part of his vegetable garden and most of the fruit bushes were enclosed in bird traps of one sort or another, and it was a full-time job for whoever was at home to keep an eye on the traps, remove any captured birds, fit each with a numbered metal ring around one leg, and record all the necessary information before each was released. I have often wondered how many cakes burned or pans boiled over while my mother was in sole charge of the ringing station!

Little wonder perhaps that with this background I became a biologist, married another biologist, and have devoted time and attention to such garden as has been available in whatever part of the world we have lived.

This developed into an especial interest in Freetown, Sierra Leone, where we not only made a fair-sized garden, but also tried to find out what shared it with us. Biologists newly arrived in a tropical country and bewildered by the array of unfamiliar plants and animals, first satisfy their curiosity by looking closely at the most accessible habitat, and indeed there may be no need to go further than the garden to be kept employed and interested full-time. In Freetown, our preoccupation with the garden involved running several sorts of traps for catching insects, both by day and by night, using a fine net stretched between two poles (known as a mist-net) to catch birds, and hand-netting butterflies. Each butterfly was marked on the wing with a felt pen – a harmless procedure – before releasing, so that it would only be recorded once. The numbers of individuals and species mounted up so rapidly that it was a challenge to go on catching more; it became a way of life, obvious to anyone passing on the road, and I was even referred to, by someone who had not heard my name, as 'the butterfly lady'.

Hand-netting butterflies in an African garden led to an intriguing discovery: the common butterflies included both forest and open country species, and there were more species of butterfly per unit area than in nearby forest, although tropical forest is a rich habitat by any standard. This posed a question as to why a garden should be so rich, and consideration of the nature of gardens and gardening suggested an answer. Even quite a small garden is a patchwork of sunny and shaded places, incorporating certain aspects of both forest and open country habitats, and flowering plants cultivated for colour and for cutting provide an unusual concentration of food for flower-feeders. Growth is so luxuriant in the hot, humid climate of Freetown that it is continually necessary to cut back shrubs, including native plants used as larval foodplants by butterflies. Production of new leaves is normally seasonal, but repeated pruning results in continuous production of tender growth palatable to small caterpillars. The effect of my gardening activities was thus to prolong the breeding season of several species of butterflies. I began to appreciate that gardening creates a unique habitat; it is man-made and managed, yet extraordinarily diverse, and provides a rich habitat for animals, particularly insects.

On returning to England after many years abroad, the West African experience freshly in mind, the backyard was the place to rediscover the English flora and fauna. Once installed as the owner rather than the temporary cultivator of a plot of land, it was only natural to approach the garden not simply as a source of flowers and produce, as space for

relaxation and for children to play, but also as a habitat to be developed
and managed to maximize its biological richness and interest.

My garden

The garden, which occupies 658 square metres surrounding the house,
was laid out in 1927, and although there have been some changes in the
arrangement of paths, lawns and flower beds, and differences from year
to year in the choice of annual and biennial flowers and vegetables, it has
probably been much the same as it is now for the past forty years or
more. In other words, on moving to Leicester in 1971, I acquired a
mature suburban garden, and was by no means starting from scratch as
far as creating a habitat was concerned. The garden is situated at a
corner on a busy road, less than four kilometres from the city centre, but
within 800 metres of farms and open fields. Nearby is a small stream
shaded by tall trees, and there are two small parks with mature trees and
large areas of grass within a radius of 450 metres. Like other well-
established gardens in the neighbourhood, it is a complex mosaic of
open spaces and shade, a medley of mini-habitats: there are flower beds
and vegetable patches, flowering as well as evergreen shrubs, a well-
trimmed lawn, fruit bushes and an old apple tree, a tangle of brambles
and nettles, tall cypress trees screening the garden from the road,
rockeries, a compost heap, well-swept paths, and until recently a small
pond. I have tried to make the garden as hospitable and attractive as
possible to insects and other wildlife, but have not changed its basic
lay-out and overall appearance. It remains a typical, medium-sized
garden, and although it is lusher, with denser vegetation, than many
neighbouring gardens, it is in no sense wild or unkempt.

My garden is part of the complex, varied sprawl of suburbia that
surrounds all towns and cities, and increasingly encroaches on the
countryside. The gardens of towns and cities, and to a varying extent
those of the suburbs, are affected as habitats by the presence of roads,
buildings and traffic, by the covering of a large proportion of the soil with
concrete and other reflective, non-absorptive materials, and by the
heating systems and machines employed by the concentration of people
that live there. These features of urbanization have a small but measur-
able effect on the climate of towns and cities, apart from any contamination of air, soil and water by dust, soot particles and alien chemicals.
With 'clean air' policies, smogs are a thing of the past, but many
fuel-burning processes lead to increased levels of sulphur dioxide,
carbon monoxide and carbon dioxide in the air of cities, and sulphur

dioxide tends to dissolve in rain and thus increase the acidity of soils. Apart from these chemical changes in the environment, heat production and covering of the soil have an effect on climate: cities on average are warmer, less humid, and less windy than surrounding rural areas, although tall buildings create local eddies and updraughts; they receive slightly more rain, but most of it falls on hard surfaces from which it drains away, so that soils tend to have a low moisture content and rather easily dry out; and they are more cloudy, more foggy, and therefore receive less solar radiation. Thus the potential of a garden not only varies with the prevailing climate, soil and topography of the area, but also depends on whether it is in the country or town. To be fair, little is known about the way in which city climates and pollution levels affect garden plants and animals, but they undoubtedly exert an influence.

A number of differences from usual gardening procedure enhance my garden as a habitat. I grow many plants with flowers that are particularly attractive to insects, keep pruning and other clearing activities to a minimum, encourage plants, including so-called weeds, that give continuous soil cover, use no herbicides, insecticides or other poisonous chemicals, and follow the ancient gardening practice of mixing vegetables and ornamental flowers. The overall result is a dense, varied and colourful stand of vegetation, offset by carefully maintained lawns and paths which preserve the impression of order.

A tolerant attitude towards self-sown wild and naturalized plants – the conventional gardener's weeds – does not produce chaos. My attitude towards 'weeds' is selective, and any that get out of hand are restricted. For instance, grasses and sow-thistles are quickly uprooted, but poppies, evening primroses and feverfew, although thinned, are left both for their flowers and as valuable cover. Since 1975, I have kept a list of flowering plants growing in the garden; many are intentionally planted, but at least 80 species have colonized of their own accord, adding to the richness of the flora. Thus far, I have recorded a total of 331 species of 74 families, 148 of them native to the British Isles and 183 aliens. Not all have been present at the same time, and in any one year there are about 250 species. The aliens have come from many different countries, and most, though not all, have been intentionally introduced to Britain. Native plants include not only thistles, ragwort, willowherb and other 'weeds', but also horticultural varieties of mezereon or daphne, shrubby cinquefoil and cabbage. On the other hand, aliens include both the majority of cultivated flowers, herbs, shrubs and vegetables, and also such vigorous weeds as Canadian fleabane (*Conyza canadensis*), buttonweed (*Cotula coronopifolia*) and pink oxalis (*Oxalis corymbosa*).

Identifying all the plants that grow in a garden is an absorbing occupation, but it is a small task compared with finding and identifying all the animals that live there. Essentially this means learning about garden insects, for as in all terrestrial habitats, they are by far the predominant group of animals. Finding out about them involves not only careful and persistent observation, but also the use of various sorts of traps, for in most cases insects can only be identified to species by close examination, often using a lens or microscope, and it is only by trapping that numbers can be accurately monitored. Casual inspection of gardens suggests that they harbour a rich insect fauna and may therefore be of considerable significance for conservation. Detailed investigations are necessary to establish whether this is indeed the case, so in the long term, trapping is in the interests of conservation. Despite enormous gaps in my knowledge, it is probably true to say that more is known about the animals that inhabit my garden, about what they are, their comings and goings, their numbers and what they are doing, than is known for any other comparably sized area.

For ten years, a tent-like construction called a Malaise trap, which catches insects that fly in through the open sides, has been operated in the same spot from 1 April to 31 October; this trap, which is a conspicuous feature of the garden, prompting puzzled enquiries or imaginative suggestions from passers-by as to its function, has provided fundamental information on the diversity, abundance and seasonality of garden insects. Another trap that depends upon attraction to a bright light has proved the main source of information about night-flying insects, particularly moths, and a variety of insects has been attracted into traps using such aromatic baits as rotting fruit and fish offal. Plastic cups sunk into the ground so that the rim is flush with the soil surface, function as pitfall traps for beetles and other ground-dwellers, and in several summers a concerted effort has been made to hand-net and mark as many as possible of the butterflies that enter the garden. Continual trapping and persistent observation are time-consuming, and particular trapping methods become as much a part of activity in the garden at certain seasons as the gardening that maintains the habitat that is the setting for the investigations.

The essence of gardening

Few human societies live in equilibrium with their environments, and industrial societies in particular impose change on their surroundings rather than adjusting to them. The effects of human activities on animal and plant communities are most dramatic where any sort of construction or development project is concerned. Building of roads, factories, new towns and airports involves wholesale removal of vegetation, drainage, earthworks and encasing the soil in concrete; the destruction of habitat, of plants and of animals attending such development projects is inevitable. It is however easy to assume that using land to grow desirable plants has little impact on animal life. Nothing could be further from the truth, although the effects of different sorts of cultivation are not the same.

In western Europe, North America, and indeed wherever cash crops or timber trees are grown or stock is pastured on a large scale, economic considerations lead relentlessly to simplification of the habitat. Farming and forestry produce, and indeed work to produce, large areas carrying just one sort of plant; monocultures, whether of grass, trees or an edible plant, are rare in nature. Farmers anxious to improve efficiency of production eliminate variety in vegetation, and hence of habitat, by such procedures as hedge-grubbing, drainage of marshy areas and application of herbicides. The creation of vast monocultures reduces the variety of plant-feeders, and the fauna is further impoverished by widespread application of pesticides to which many predatory insects and other animals are susceptible. Thus by establishing monocultures, agriculture dramatically simplifies not only the plant but also the animal community of an area.

Gardening, however, has the opposite effect on the composition of flora and hence of fauna, since most gardeners strive for maximum diversity within even a tiny plot, aiming to produce a colourful display in the herbaceous border, as well as vegetables, fruit, herbs, and almost certainly a lawn. A few gardeners may establish monocultures, perhaps favouring roses, or putting all their land under grass, but since it is unlikely that any two have identical tastes, they contribute to the overall variety of vegetation in a residential area. Many gardeners are collectors in the sense that they make continual additions to their garden flora over the years by establishing cuttings, roots or seedlings of plants admired in others' gardens, so that a well-established garden contains more species of plants than the area would support had it been left undisturbed. Many cultivated garden plants (in whatever country) are introductions from other parts of the world, and since the processes of clearing, digging, hoeing and watering the soil render it continually receptive to seeds and favour the establishment, at least temporarily, of local wild plants (as weeds), gardening can be regarded as a process of enrichment of the vegetation, in marked contrast to the simplification that attends agriculture.

I have no doubt that, were my garden abandoned, in thirty years' time it would be a dense mixed scrub of birch, holly, ash, elder and hawthorn, with brambles, bittersweet, nettles, several sorts of grass, and perhaps creeping thistle, smooth hawk's-beard and yarrow in the more open places. Successive changes in the vegetation would lead eventually to the establishment of the particular plant association, or climax community, characteristic of central England. As it is, the garden supports all these plants and many more, twenty times this number, although the weeds, like the cultivated plants, come and go from year to year, by chance and as conditions change. As a consequence of the enormous variety in the flora of a garden, there are plants to satisfy a range of herbivorous (plant-feeding) insects, and these in turn support an array of predators and parasites. The greater variety of plants found in a garden than in the same area left undisturbed therefore supports an extraordinarily rich insect fauna, almost certainly richer than the area would shelter if covered with native vegetation. Gardening leads to enrichment not only of the flora but also of the fauna, insects in particular, in contrast to farming which simplifies both plant and animal communities, and impoverishes much of the countryside.

Animal residents and visitors
In a garden there is scope for feeding in many different ways, as well as an array of potential sheltering and breeding sites – in shade, in open places, in the pond, in the compost heap, in leaf litter, below stones, and so on. Gardens offer particular opportunities to insects, although they harbour many other sorts of invertebrates, from spiders and woodlice to slugs and snails. Birds exploit gardens, including those in towns, more fully than other vertebrate animals, and an astonishing variety of birds may pass through a mature garden during the course of a year. Mammals, from hedgehogs and moles to squirrels and foxes, are regular garden visitors in many areas, foxes in particular attracting disproportionate attention and interest especially in urban areas. Less conspicuous are frogs and newts, for which garden ponds have become an important refuge with the draining or contamination of many field

ponds. In terms of dependence upon the habitat and exploitation of what it can offer, insects and birds are the predominant garden animals, and it is these two groups about which I know most in my garden.

A feature of the animal community of gardens, arising in part from the short-term seasonal availability of such resources as flowers and seeds, is the way in which its composition fluctuates. Both individuals and species of insects and birds come and go, producing variations from day to day, from month to month, and also from one year to the next. Long-term changes in the garden animal community represent adjustments to changes in the flora and to modification of the habitat caused by gardening. The introduction of a new plant species is likely to lead to the establishment of plant-feeders new to the garden, perhaps a different species of aphid; this will diversify the feeding opportunities for predators of aphids, such as hoverfly larvae, which in turn creates additional scope for small ichneumonid wasps that parasitize hoverflies. In other words, an addition to the flora can lead to additions to the fauna. This is because all animals are ultimately dependent on green plants for food; some eat plants directly, others are predators, but their prey, or their prey's prey, eat plants. Green plants, however, use light energy to manufacture simple sugars and other organic substances from carbon dioxide and water, in the process of photosynthesis, and elaborate them into more complicated compounds. The carbohydrates, fats and proteins that animals acquire in their food have all ultimately been derived from the products of photosynthesis. Green plants are producers; the animals that eat them, and each other, are consumers. Each species of plant is the starting point for a series of feeding interactions, such as plant – aphid – hoverfly – ichneumonid wasp, known as a food chain. Continual change in the varied garden flora is likely to generate change throughout the animal community as new food chains are established.

Events outside a garden also have an impact on the composition of its fauna. In warm, dry summers, when aphids feeding on agricultural crops do particularly well, their predators, such as hoverflies and ladybirds, may experience population explosions. As they deplete the supply of aphids, or when the crops are harvested, vast numbers of hoverflies and ladybirds leave the fields and move into gardens. Any disruption of events in the countryside in summer, whether caused by human activities or extreme weather, tends to displace insects, many of which subsequently appear in gardens. There may be influxes of common and familiar species, or isolated occurrences of unusual butterflies or other insects, far from their usual haunts. The wealth of

feeding opportunities, especially for nectar-feeders, make gardens a
haven for refugees from the countryside, and there is always a chance of
finding a rarity. Good crops of flowers or seeds bring occasional visitors
into my garden, such as a hummingbird hawk moth, delicately probing
honeysuckle flowers with its long tongue, or goldfinches pecking the
seeds from teasels. Occasional visitors and temporary colonizers are
very much a feature of gardens. I can never sit back, confident that I
know the garden fauna, for it may change tomorrow.

Insects – friend or foe?

Despite a general interest in wildlife and conservation, most people have
ambivalent attitudes towards the animals that share their gardens or
enter their houses, and in particular to insects. Brightly coloured
butterflies are widely admired and welcomed in gardens, but the white
butterflies whose caterpillars eat cabbages and other brassicas are
viewed with distaste. In many parts of the British Isles, white butterflies
were once given the names of unpopular groups of people – in Lincoln-
shire they were 'Frenchmen'!

There is a widespread tendency to categorize insects as 'useful' or
'harmful', and to tolerate or eradicate them accordingly. Wasps are
regarded as nasty because they sting, ants because there are so many of
them, and a whole multitude of bugs and beetles because they live on
fruit, vegetables or flowers. I know a number of otherwise sensible
people who become hysterical when a moth flutters around them, and
this may derive from the ancient belief that moths are the souls of the
dead. Some insects are discriminated against because of their appearance: in Dorset, for instance, children used to kill powdery-looking
moths (known as millers) while chanting a slanderous rhyme about the
honesty, or lack of it, of flour-millers. A black beetle on a path is all too
often intentionally crushed underfoot, but ask why, and the usual
response is puzzlement that the action should even be questioned,
although no justification is forthcoming. Bees, however, despite their
ability to sting, are accepted as useful because of their pollinating and
honey-making activities.

The truth is that categorization of insects and other animals as
'goodies' and 'baddies' is a misrepresentation stemming from ignorance
and a measure of anthropocentric arrogance. Certainly the common
social wasps can inflict painful stings, but they also catch and feed
caterpillars, including those of cabbage whites, to their larvae; and
although cabbage white caterpillars eat garden crops, they become

butterflies which assist in transfer of pollen from flower to flower as they feed. Ants in and around houses are a nuisance if they find an open jam pot or the Sunday joint, but they are scavengers, cleaning up dropped fragments of food, insect corpses and all sorts of organic debris. There is no such thing as a useful or harmful insect; they all interact in a variety of ways with their environment, and sometimes their habits accord with our interests, sometimes they do not. With understanding and tolerance, it is possible to live happily with garden insects and other animals: the surest way of avoiding a wasp sting is not to interfere with a wasp; the easiest way of protecting the Sunday joint or a pot of jam from ants, is to cover them; and, as I shall explain in a later chapter, inter-cropping vegetables with other plants reduces losses to herbivores such as the caterpillars of cabbage white butterflies.

Nevertheless, some insects can become a nuisance or even a danger. Economic and social interests necessitate eradication, or at least deterrence, of those that pose a threat to health, food supply, structure, furnishings, clothing, or to some commercial enterprise. It is difficult, however, to justify chemical warfare in an ordinary domestic garden, where the distribution of poisons may have unintended and undesirable results. The problem is that the widely used organo-chlorine pesticides (which include dieldrin and DDT) are non-biodegradable: in other words, they are not broken down by the normal processes of digestion or decomposition, but persist as poisons, either accumulating in the soil, or becoming concentrated as they pass along food chains.

A poison may be applied at quite low concentrations, just enough to kill defoliating caterpillars or some other pest; but songbirds that eat poisoned caterpillars assimilate the organo-chlorine poisons contained in every caterpillar they eat; and a bird of prey which eats such birds receives the cumulative dose ingested by all of its prey. Declines in the numbers of sparrowhawks, peregrines and other birds of prey during the 1960s have been attributed to the widespread use of organo-chlorine pesticides: some birds were poisoned outright, but others became infertile or laid thin-shelled eggs which broke in the nest during incubation. The use of DDT is now discouraged in Britain, although it is still exported to Third World countries; it is so persistent that it is believed that all that has ever been applied is still around somewhere, in soils, water or living organisms. When a persistent poison of this sort is ingested by an earthworm along with soil and leaf litter, it accumulates in the worm's tissues; although the worm may survive, a thrush that eats hundreds of earthworms receives hundreds of times the amount of poison, sometimes with fatal results, and the outlook for a cat that eats such a thrush is not good. Indiscriminate use of poisons not only puts at risk the garden birds, it is also a potential threat to pets, let alone to inquisitive children or to the gardener who is not over-fussy about washing his hands. Moreover, there is evidence that predators such as centipedes and spiders, which help control caterpillars and other plant-feeders, are more susceptible to organo-chlorine poisons than the caterpillars that prompt their use. Consequently the application of pesticides may be a one-way road, with no turning and no going back, as their use increases the need to use them.

So I use no poisons in my garden. There are losses, particularly to slugs in wet years, but to me the garden is a habitat to which I must adjust rather than a territory to be conquered. I am quite happy with this arrangement and, to judge by the luxuriance of vegetation and abundance of insects and other animals, so are the plants and animals that share with me this particular plot of land.

A landscape of gardens

Nowhere in the world is gardening developed as a pastime, preoccupation, and indeed obsession, to the extent that it is in Britain. As a leisure activity, it is second only to watching television, and forms a major outlet of private expenditure as witnessed by the burgeoning of garden centres and nurseries where, in England alone, we probably spend more than £200 million a year. In contrast to many other Europeans, the British have resisted planners' attempts to house them in high-density blocks of flats, and the main reason for this seems to be determination to own and cultivate a plot of land, however small. It is ironic that widely supported endeavours to preserve wildlife and conserve the countryside against the encroachment of urban development, are made more difficult by this insistence on traditional peasant rights to a piece of private land. There are more than 15 million gardens in Britain, most of them small, a few very large, and eighty per cent of households have a garden attached. They constitute a rich and varied habitat, dispersed and fragmented, but covering more than 400,000 hectares in England and Wales, nearly three per cent of the total land area. They are a major feature of the landscape, and of great significance for wildlife in a small, crowded island where wildlife conservation is a major concern.

Many people confuse conservation of flora and fauna with designation of beautiful and remote areas for leisure and recreation; they want to be able to stride across the open hills far from crowds and traffic, and seek to protect such 'wilderness' areas. But the hills of England, Wales and much of Scotland were once forested, and owe their present starkness to tree-felling and sheep-farming; in many ways they are as unnatural as a garden. Moreover, the 'traditional' lowland patchwork of small field and hedgerow, though well-established, is only about 200 years old. The landscape that many strive to conserve, whether the open hills or the peaceful rural pattern of meadow, copse, hedgerow and lane, is man-made. The flora and fauna of the countryside are under threat from the activities of an affluent, industrialized society, but gardens, unlike rural and wilderness areas, are in no sense a threatened habitat. On the contrary, the British defend and maintain them, and total garden area is extending with new housing developments. Consequently, gardens play an increasing role in wildlife conservation, or can do, with more understanding of who lives there and exactly what they are doing.

I

JANUARY

Looking forward

Much as I love my garden, and fascinating as I find its animal inhabitants, there is rarely much incentive to leave the warmth and light of the fireside and venture outside in the dead of winter. In mild winters, vegetation is dank and sodden, much of it blackened and decaying where it stands; I slip and slide on dead leaves accumulated on the paths, and the lawn is like a wet sponge which oozes water into the imprints of my feet. Cold winter days are often bright, but the ground is hard as stone, and the garden's brittle charm is more comfortably viewed through the windows, especially from the circle of warmth around a log fire.

One of the bonuses of a well-grown garden is the quantity of small logs and kindling it provides. In ten years an amazing number of trees have had to be felled, yet this has made little difference to the overall appearance of my garden, an indication of its high productivity. Three of the elderly Lawson's cypresses in the front garden had to go when they lost their grip on the soil, and leaned at a dangerous angle over the pavement; a small apple tree, self-seeded birches, hollies, hawthorns and a sycamore have at different times had adverse effects on surrounding plants, not to mention the efficiency with which the thirsty roots of one birch blocked a drain-pipe; in the severe winter of 1978-9 two of the largest buddleia bushes died; and several wych elms planted in 1972 later succumbed to Dutch elm disease. Cutting down young trees seems almost wickedly destructive, but where allowed, the cut stumps of broad-leafed trees have sprouted to create miniature coppices that provide shelter and an abundance of tender food for leaf-eaters.

By January it seems essential to have a bonfire, something I put off for as long as possible. Within the limits of time and patience, I sort vegetation when it is cleared in the autumn, to ensure that everything that will rot becomes compost and only the really recalcitrant woody, fibrous or thorny waste is left to dry out for later burning. Burning appeals to my tidy nature, for it disposes of an ugly and enormous tangle of garden refuse, but I try and restrict it, because so many nutrients are dispersed wastefully in the smoke and gases rising from a bonfire. Ideally bonfires are built on soil so that nutrients in the ash are not wasted, but as my garden becomes more and more densely planted, this becomes less and less easy to arrange, and it is sometimes necessary to burn rubbish on an area of crazy paving at the end of the garden. My assiduous efforts with dust-pan and brush to collect the precious ash before it is dispersed by wind and rain are never entirely successful, and the bellflower, which has colonized the cracks between the stones, thrives on the input of nutrients.

This is the time for planning and looking ahead to a new season in which of course the garden will be better and more productive than last year! My planning and anticipation encompass not only gardening as such, but also various projects for finding out about garden animals. I can capitalize on the results of last year's trapping and monitoring of garden insects to decide what investigations are worthwhile for this year and when they should be undertaken. I wish I found it as easy to learn from previous years' gardening activities. Those beautifully illustrated seed catalogues, rich with evocative names and bountiful promise, carry me away on flights of fancy every year, ready to accept the most extravagant claims for yield, colour, early fruiting or ease of cultivation. The lessons of last year go unheeded: I shall have one more try at growing courgettes; surely outdoor tomatoes will fruit earlier this year; and I shall find a way of protecting delphinium seedlings from slugs without resort to poisons. Optimism flourishes, but unfortunately many schemes have relevance and practicality when discussed by the fireside that they lose in the cold light of a working day.

Weather and energies allowing, some of the coming year's plans can be put into effect whenever the ground is free of snow and the soil is soft enough to take a spade. Most of the beds in which vegetables were planted have been cleared by now, and can be roughly dug, leaving rain and frost to continue the job of breaking up the soil. The two small lawns that originally occupied much of the front garden were dug over in early January in different years, as was part of the main lawn. The lawns were sacrificed simply to give more room for planting flowers and vegetables and, inevitably, the remaining lawn is sometimes viewed speculatively – but as though the thought had taken shape, there is immediate protest that there will be nowhere left for sunbathing or picnicking, and not enough space for swingball or badminton, so ambition is stifled, and the lawn stays as it is.

For much of January the garden seems barren and dead, and in a hard winter even privet loses its leaves. Plants are lying dormant, and apart from a few birds, it would seem that all the animals have disappeared or departed like the swifts. And yet inside the house a small bright blob on the window-sill unfolds legs and crawls unhurriedly up the window-pane – a 2-spot ladybird hibernating indoors has had its winter sleep broken by the warmth of the house.

The long sleep

Birds and many mammals remain active throughout the winter, provided they have adequate food as a source of energy, and shelter from severe weather. They can do this because they are able to maintain a constant body temperature and high rate of metabolism (biochemical activity); they are homoiothermic, a term popularly translated as warm-blooded. In contrast, reptiles, amphibians (frogs, toads and newts), and invertebrates, such as insects, cool down or heat up as the temperature around them alters, and become inactive in cold weather as their metabolic rate falls; they are poikilothermic, a condition sometimes misleadingly described as cold-blooded. They have no option but to hibernate, passing the winter months in a state of suspended animation, neither moving nor feeding, with a metabolic rate so low that there is little drain on their fat reserves. A few mammals seek a secure refuge and become poikilothermic in winter: as their internal temperature falls, breathing rate and heart beat slow right down and they become torpid. This is an adaptation for avoiding conditions that are unfavourable, usually because insufficient food is available. Bats hibernate in the roofs of buildings or in hollow trees, becoming quite cold to the touch, and hedgehogs hibernate curled up in leaf litter or in a moss-lined hole, using fat reserves laid down in the preceding season to provide energy for essential life processes. Hedgehogs sometimes wake up if disturbed, but then need to feed if they are to get through the winter; I suspect that it is sleepy but hungry hedgehogs that scatter cabbage leaves and orange peel from the compost heap as they delve into the worm-laden layers below. Squirrels and wood mice remain active in the winter using stocks of stored food, although wood mice sleep through severe cold spells. Squirrels betray their presence in winter by leaving apple boughs stripped of bark which they have gnawed away to get at the nutritious tissue beneath.

Most garden insects pass the winter in an inactive, non-feeding form, i.e. as eggs or pupae, but some hibernate as adults. One of the most impressive of these is the brimstone butterfly, which I suspect hibernates in this or neighbouring gardens, although so far their hiding places have eluded me. On an icy January day, I came across one deep in a tangle of brambles growing in a disused railway cutting not far away. It was clinging motionless, wings tightly closed, beneath an arching bramble stem, looking much like a bleached, dead leaf; to complete the illusion, both bramble and butterfly were encrusted with hoar-frost and beadlets of ice. Peacock and tortoiseshell butterflies hibernate in dry, sheltered places, and this is why they can often be found fluttering around in the garage, potting shed or house in the autumn or spring. The aphid-eating larvae of some species of hoverflies hibernate, and I often find small green or brown larvae deep within clumps of saxifrage or ivy. They leave aphid-infested plants when they are fully fed, and wait out the winter in the shelter of dense ground vegetation, without moving or feeding. When temperatures rise in the spring, they turn into pupae, and development of the adult fly proceeds.

Adult insects become active whenever it is warm enough, and so hibernation is often interrupted, especially in late winter. The likelihood of this happening depends on temperature and snowfall, and consequently varies greatly from year to year. Sometimes on a January day warm enough to tempt me to stroll round the garden, I surprise a solitary tortoiseshell basking on a sunny wall, or a drone fly visiting an early-flowering crocus for an unseasonal meal of pollen. As the damp, grey mound of lavender cotton (*Santolina*) steams in the sun, bright moving spots appear, as though it is about to burst into flame. I blink hard, look again, and see dozens of red ladybirds, mostly 7-spots and a few 11-spots, crawling from the tangled mass of stems. The warmth has woken them up, although they do not fly so early in the year.

Waste not, want not
Renewal of growth and activity in the garden would not be possible without recycling of materials essential for life, which are returned again and again to the soil after passing along food chains. Plants manufacture sugars and other more complex organic substances, including starch, cellulose, lignin, fats, pigments, and many sorts of proteins, but to do this they need access to a whole range of different chemical elements, which they absorb as salts in solution through their roots. Although

carbon dioxide is abundantly available in the atmosphere, the continuation of production of new plant material is dependent upon constant replenishment of the elements that a plant requires from the soil. Most gardeners and farmers restore what they have taken from the soil by application of purchased or prepared fertilizers, but natural areas, whether woodland or meadow, remain productive without such intervention. Nitrogen, phosphorus and other essential chemical elements are released from dead plants, animal corpses and faeces by the feeding activities of a vast array of organisms, ranging from bacteria and fungi to earthworms and maggots. Feeders on dead organic matter are often referred to as decomposers, since they break down complex organic compounds into simple substances, all of which are ultimately returned to the soil.

Recycling of essential materials is fundamental to life on earth. All elements, even abundant ones like carbon and nitrogen, exist in finite amounts, and are used again and again in the building of organisms. Some cycles, such as the carbon cycle, are fairly simple. Carbon in the form of carbon dioxide is obtained by green plants from the atmosphere and fixed during photosynthesis as various sorts of organic compounds. When an animal eats a plant or another animal, whether alive or dead, the complex organic compounds in its food are dismantled by the processes of digestion, and then reassembled in its tissues to meet its individual requirements. Plants, herbivores, carnivores and decomposers all release carbon dioxide back to the atmosphere when they split sugar molecules for the release of energy in the process of respiration. Carbon is recycled on a massive scale, since more than twelve tons of carbon may be fixed per hectare per year on land by photosynthesis. During certain episodes in the geological past, dead trees and marine organisms accumulated without decomposing; carbon was locked up in coal or oil, and it is only now being released as carbon dioxide when fossil fuels are burned.

Most elements, however, never pass into the atmosphere: calcium salts are acquired in solution by plants through their roots, animals acquire calcium by eating plants or other animals and by drinking, and decomposition results in its return to water and soil. Calcium carbonate is a major component of skeletons and shells, where it may remain locked up after the animal that formed them has died and its soft parts decomposed. Under certain marine conditions in the past, shells accumulated, becoming consolidated and compressed, and eventually forming rock. Earth movements have raised sea-beds into dry land, where rain and ground water gradually wear away chalk and limestone, once again releasing calcium.

Other cycles are much more complicated, involving many steps and alternative pathways. One of these, the nitrogen cycle, is of great significance for the gardener, first because nitrogen is a constituent of all protein and therefore essential for growth, and secondly because a whole range of gardening events and practices affects its supply and availability. Gaseous nitrogen is present in abundance in the atmosphere, but plants can only use nitrogen compounds in solution, which they absorb through their roots, sometimes as ammonia but usually as nitrates; animals depend upon nitrogen compounds mainly proteins, in their food. There are three routes by which nitrates are formed: by so-called nitrifying bacteria, which use ammonia released into soil when dead plants and animals decompose; by blue-green algae and nitrogen-fixing bacteria, abundant in most soils, from atmospheric nitrogen; and, to a variable extent, by the action of lightning on atmospheric nitrogen. Not all nitrogen-fixing bacteria are free-living; many sorts of *Rhizobium* invade the roots of different members of the Leguminosae (the pea and bean family), forming characteristic nodules which are pinkish-red inside. Since nodule-forming bacteria make atmospheric nitrogen available to a plant, leguminous plants can be grown on soils deficient in nitrates. As well as accumulating nitrogen compounds, legumes enrich the soil around their roots with nitrates, and this is why they are used in crop-rotation schemes. Soils also contain denitrifying bacteria which use nitrates as a source of energy, converting them into gaseous nitrogen in the process; these bacteria, unlike nitrifying and nitrogen-fixing bacteria, do not require oxygen, and thrive in water-logged soil which consequently quickly loses its fertility.

Thus, application of composted plant remains or manure as a source of ammonia, crop rotation or inter-planting with legumes, and working the soil to improve drainage and promote aeration, all help to maintain the nitrate content of garden soil through the agency of bacteria. Beware, however, of using straw or other fibrous plant material in lieu of compost, because its carbon content is high relative to nitrogen. Soil micro-organisms use the carbon as an energy source and increase in numbers, but in so doing quickly exhaust the nitrogen compounds in the straw and then extract nitrates from the soil. Nitrogen locked up in the cells of micro-organisms is immobilized as far as plants are concerned. It is of course released eventually when the micro-organisms die, but in the short term nitrogen fertilizers may be necessary.

The fate of dead leaves

Measurements of accumulation and disappearance of dead plant material in woodland give some indication of what is happening in a garden. Land vegetation consists largely of woody supporting tissues which few herbivores can digest, and 90 per cent or more of the organic matter formed in a forest as a consequence of photosynthesis is used as food when it is dead, i.e. by decomposers. Every year, between 500,000 and one million kilograms of organic matter, in the form of leaf and branch fall and root production, is added to each square kilometre of soil in temperate deciduous forest. Yet this mass of plant material soon decomposes and the nutrients it contains are released for recycling.

By the end of the growing season, the garden contains an enormous accumulation of dead vegetation; as the days pass, its tidy, well-maintained summer aspect deteriorates, and it becomes rather a mess. Leaves fall, herbaceous plants die back, and the ground becomes shrouded in plant litter of one sort or another. The immediate response is to start clearing the herbaceous beds, sweeping up leaves, and tidying away all the unsightly debris. Many gardeners burn most that they remove, scenting the autumn air with their bonfires or, all too often, creating acrid palls of smoke that drive their neighbours indoors. But if normal processes of decomposition are allowed to take place, most of the dead vegetation will rot away, and only the most fibrous and woody material persists for any length of time and may therefore reasonably be burned. In meadows, hedgerows and woods, there is short-term accumulation of leaf litter and dead plants, but it soon disappears, as a result of the feeding activities of decomposers. If the nitrogen cycle is proceeding unimpeded, the same should happen in a garden which will not therefore need any addition of nitrogen fertilizer. It seems profligate to make the purchase of fertilizer necessary by burning all dead material.

If left alone, much of the garden vegetation decomposes where it falls, releasing nutrients into the soil. This often seems to me more direct (and less back-breaking) than carting it all to the compost heap and then having to return later in the winter with heavy bucketfuls of wet compost. (A wheelbarrow would not help me, as my garden is on a slope with several flights of steps to negotiate.) The events attending decomposition and release of nutrients are much the same in the soil and in a compost heap, although the breakdown of dead plant material may be more rapid and complete in a compost heap, where decomposers are concentrated, than in litter left lying on the soil. On the one hand, it is obviously tidier to concentrate rotting vegetation in one place, but on the other, it is less effort to leave it where it falls; the choice is really between an even scatter of nutrients or a massive input for one part of the garden.

Dry, dead leaves on paths, scurried around by the wind, retain their shape and substance for weeks if not months, but as soon as they get wet, they begin to change colour and texture, becoming darker and slimy to the touch. Water not only softens the tissues of a leaf, but also rinses out tannins and other toxic chemicals so that it becomes palatable to such animals as earthworms, millipedes and woodlice, and more accessible to bacteria and fungi. The speed and efficiency with which microscopic decomposers break down dead material is greatly improved by the activities of larger invertebrate decomposers. In experiments involving the burying of leaf litter in bags made of netting with different sized mesh, leaves in bags of mesh so fine as to admit only micro-organisms showed no signs of breakdown even after nine months, whereas decomposition was well advanced in coarse mesh bags after only three months. The feeding activities of larger decomposers, such as earthworms, fragment dead leaves so that they become more accessible to bacteria and fungi which are able to complete the chemical breakdown of leaf tissue. All decomposers are simply using dead plants and animals or their products, such as faeces, as a source of nutrients and energy, in other words as food. Bacteria and fungi, however, do not eat as we normally understand the word, since they have neither mouth nor digestive tract. They live on or even within their food, onto which they release digestive enzymes and from which they absorb such products of digestion as they need. Thus the activities of micro-organisms feeding on dead leaves inevitably release nutrients into the soil.

A dead leaf soon loses its characteristic chemistry under the combined effects of softening by water, autolysis (self-digestion) and the activities of decomposers. As decomposition proceeds, dead plant material whatever its origin becomes more and more similar, and consequently decomposers, from bacteria to earthworms, are indiscriminate in their feeding habits compared, say, with caterpillars, which are often restricted to one plant species. Micro-organisms, however, are highly selective as to which carbon compounds they use as energy sources, although not their origin. Some bacteria and fungi, for instance, use sugars, some use starch, and others use cellulose, the complex carbohydrate that forms plant cell walls and which few animals can digest. As the chemical structure of a leaf is broken down, its potential as food becomes more and more restricted. Sugars are used up first, cellulose is broken down fairly quickly, and finally only lignin, the compound that gives wood its tough, fibrous composition, remains. The number of micro-organisms that can digest lignin is limited, and much is incorporated into the soil where, however, soil fungi continue to work on it. About ten per cent of the surface litter in a forest is incorporated into the soil as humus, a complex organic substance composed of lignin and its derivatives, tightly combined with nitrogenous compounds. Humus is slowly decomposed by micro-organisms, but as it is constantly replaced from litter, the proportion of humus in soil remains unchanged from year to year. It is a vital constituent of fertile soil, not only as a source of nutrients, but also because it binds mineral particles together giving a crumbly texture. In a garden where all dead plant material is cleared away and destroyed, the soil quality eventually deteriorates as its humus content is depleted.

The processes by which nutrients from leaf litter are gradually incorporated into soil happen on a larger and more dramatic scale in a compost heap. There are those who have perfected techniques for composting dead vegetation to a fine art, involving layered applications of grass-cuttings and careful control of temperature, moisture content and aeration, but my approach is far more casual. Alongside a path, beneath the apple tree, I dig a pit about a metre square and up to 50 centimetres deep. Into this goes all the soft, non-woody garden waste including weeds with soil clinging to their roots, and all organic kitchen refuse from potato peelings to coffee grounds – but not grass-cuttings, which are left to decompose where they fall on the lawn. By late summer, the compost heap is large and the scene of obvious activity: wasps and many different sorts of flies hum around it, and when the top layers are turned over, the soil beneath is a seething tangle of the reddish earthworms known as brandlings. During autumn and winter, more and more vegetation is piled on, but by late January the heap has subsided considerably. Decomposers have broken down dead plant material, rain has washed nutrients and soil particles from the top layers, and beneath is a rich compost. Forking out compost and carrying bucketfuls around the garden are hard work, but I find it immensely satisfying and more than a little hilarious as brandlings spill and drape over the bucket's rim like peculiarly mobile spaghetti.

Underground activity

The speed with which dead vegetation disappears is testimony to the abundance of decomposers, and the numbers of brandlings in a compost heap suggest that earthworms are important. However, numerous other sorts of organisms are involved, many small enough to be easily overlooked, and most so small that they can only be seen using a microscope. Most decomposition on land takes place actually in the soil, and so we can get some idea of the contribution of different sorts of organisms from quantitative analyses of soil communities. Most of the methods used do not distinguish between organisms that feed on living material and those that decompose dead matter, but estimates of numbers of groups that include a high proportion of decomposers give some indication of their relative importance.

One gram of fertile soil contains more than one thousand million bacteria, and although fungi cannot be counted in the same way, estimates of volume suggest that their total mass is similar. The top 15 centimetres of soil beneath a square metre of permanent grassland contains nearly 200,000 arthropods, including more than a hundred thousand mites, over forty thousand collembolans (springtails), thousands of bristletails (the group that includes silverfish), and several thousand beetles and their larvae. In the same volume of soil, there may be 20 million nematode worms, up to 200,000 enchytraeids (potworms), and several hundred earthworms. This is quite apart from the millipedes, woodlice and small arthropods in the surface litter, and other groups of animals which are largely herbivorous or carnivorous.

The biomass, or total quantity, of soil communities and their composition vary from place to place and seasonally, with temperature and moisture conditions, soil acidity, vegetation, the availability of dead material, and the activities of man. In fertile garden soil, invertebrates and micro-organisms are abundant and varied, especially if litter is allowed to accumulate, and there is liberal application of compost or manure. Every square millimetre of topsoil is the scene of furious activity, but on such a microscopic scale that we are rarely aware of it. Earthworms and beetles burrow through the soil, creating their own space, but mites and tiny insects, such as collembolans, roam the air spaces between soil particles, seeking out food. The mites include active, voracious predators of other tiny soil organisms, as well as many that feed on dead material. Microscopic protozoans and aquatic animals move around in the film of water coating soil particles, ingesting algal cells, dead organic matter, or each other. Nematodes, including predators and parasites of plants and animals as well as decomposers, wriggle through moist soil, and tiny potworms and bacteria flourish wherever there is moisture and organic material they can use as food.

PLATE I   1 The garden is coming to life in May, although the lawn bed is still almost empty. Beyond is a bright pink cushion of *Phlox douglasii*, and, in the foreground, creamy rowan flowers hang over a carpet of purple *Aubretia*. 2 By September, vegetation is dense, although in this particular year the runner beans did badly. Asters and various sorts of marigolds brighten the lawn bed.

Many different sorts of fungi live in soil, each forming a diffuse mesh called a mycelium, composed of thread-like structures known as hyphae, which ramify between soil particles. The growing tips of the hyphae penetrate organic matter liberating digestive enzymes, and sugars and other nutrients are absorbed over the whole mycelium. It is virtually impossible to recognise a fungus individual, for different mycelia become intertwined forming a living network in the soil. The only time they make their presence known is when a compact mass of spore-producing hyphae pushes above ground as a toadstool.

Earthworms are of prime importance both for decomposition of dead material and for maintenance of soil texture. Not only do they fragment, distribute, bury and eat dead leaves, but they plough and work the soil. There are several common garden species, one of the most familiar being *Lumbricus terrestris*, large, fat worms, which make permanent burrows into which they drag dead leaves and twigs, often left protruding from the burrow entrance. This species has been shown to remove more than 90 per cent of annual leaf fall in an apple orchard during the following winter, amounting to more than a ton of dry leaf weight per hectare. Unlike most other animals, earthworms digest cellulose, and consequently make the most of dead plant material as food, but they bury more than they eat, which leads to improved soil fertility. The burrowing activities of earthworms aerate soil and enhance drainage, both of which improve conditions for plants and for micro-organisms, but they probably have the greatest effect on the structure of soil by eating it. They are eating excavators, burrowing by sucking soil in through their mouths, digesting much of its organic component, and excreting a mixture of finely divided soil, leaf fragments and mucus, familiar as worm casts. Many species defaecate within their burrows, where the casts help establish the crumb structure of soil. Some abundant species found in gardens back up their burrows to make castings on the soil surface, those of *Allolobophora longa* often being conspicuous on lawns. By eating soil and making surface casts, worms bring fine soil particles and nutrients to the surface.

Charles Darwin, better known for his theory of evolution, wrote a book about earthworms, entitled *The formation of vegetable mould through the action of worms, with observations on their habits*, largely based on observations he made in his garden at Down House in Kent. He was the first to realize the long-term effects that the burrowing and casting

PLATE 2   3 New growth is evident everywhere in May, but the Malaise trap dominates the garden. Forget-me-nots, spotted dead-nettle and bleeding heart (*Dicentra*) brighten the rockery and, across the road, a hawthorn tree is in flower. 4 By July, magenta *Geranium cinereum* and mats of saxifrage in the rockery are dwarfed by tall ferns, marguerite daisies and hollyhocks, and the garden is lush and green.

activities of worms have in burying stones and hence preserving archaeological remains, and the mill-stone on which he tested his theories can still be seen in his garden. His measurements of worm casts on old pasture indicate that a soil layer five millimetres thick is deposited annually on the surface. Earthworms are of immense value to the gardener. As Darwin said: 'Worms prepare the ground in an excellent manner for the growth of fibrous-rooted plants and for seedlings of all kinds. They periodically expose the mould to the air, and sift it so that no stones larger than the particles which they can swallow are left in it. They mingle the whole intimately together, like a gardener who prepares fine soil for his choicest plants. In this state it is well fitted to retain moisture and to absorb all soluble substances, as well as for the process of nitrification.'

Signs of life

At this time of year, when it is cold and food is in short supply, birds are more obvious than in the summer, and were it not for their presence the garden in winter would seem very dreary indeed. Resident birds, present throughout the year, are joined by winter visitors, and all are alert and opportunist, making the most of whatever feeding opportunities are available. Black-headed and common gulls swoop low over the garden; starlings assemble noisily to dispute possession of kitchen scraps, having already picked clean the carcass of the Christmas turkey; a wren creeps mouse-like along a bramble stem, deftly picking tiny insects and spiders from crevices; and a robin is always close by me to snatch worms as I dig or move compost. A nervous coal tit pecks insistently at a mesh bag of peanuts hanging by the kitchen window, but leaves on the arrival of a pugnacious blue tit, which is itself displaced by a 'heavy mob' of greenfinches. Fragments of peanuts fall to the ground, where a demure hedge sparrow, unable to cling to the bag of nuts, exploits the untidy feeding habits of the greenfinches. A plump bullfinch perches precariously on the dry seed-heads of last year's snapdragons, clumsily tearing them apart to get at the minute seeds, and the hedge sparrow quietly joins it, to glean the many seeds dropped onto the snowy ground beneath. One or two fieldfares or redwings may visit to rootle amongst leaf litter, the fieldfare in particular making short work of what is left of fallen apples. Prolonged freezing weather is hard on birds, and when the thaw sets in, a robin sips delicately from melt water dripping from the house roof.

Birds remain active in the cold, but by now, however bleak the winter, even the plants are showing signs of stirring life and the promise that spring will eventually come. Winter aconites push through the soil, a few wallflowers bloom, and snowdrops lift their delicate white and green heads even through a covering of snow. As the month proceeds, flower buds swell on flowering currant and forsythia bushes, daffodil and narcissus bulbs put up fat, green spikes, tightly clustered flower-heads appear on early purple sprouting broccoli, and the fragrant flowers of daphne scent the cool air. It is strange that a shrub that flowers so early should have such a sweet smell; flower scents have evolved as a means of attracting pollinating insects, yet I have never seen insect visitors at daphne flowers. It is a satisfying shrub to grow, not only because of its fragrance and colour at a time when there are few flowers, but also because it is a native shrub that is rare in the wild. Early crocuses brighten the ground with sunshine yellow, becoming a focus of interest for house sparrows. They vandalize crocuses, leaving a scatter of torn, yellow petals around a mutilated clump of flowers, apparently in their attempts to reach and eat the female part of the flower, the stigma, which contains saffron, rich in vitamin A.

Towards the end of January, as the days lengthen and – at least in some years – temperatures begin to rise, a different sort of activity heralds the approaching spring. A house sparrow collects an untidy beakful of wisps of dead grass and flies off with it, and first a thrush, then a blue tit, try a few tentative notes of song. Just as a warm day is sufficient to break insect hibernation, so it encourages birds to embark on the preliminaries to breeding, although next day, a drop in temperature may put a stop to it all. January can be characterized by the repeated starting and stopping of biological events. I get the feeling that plants and animals are bursting with pent-up energies, like a motorist halted at a red light but impatiently 'revving' the engine; at the first hint that spring is on the way, there is a burst of activity, but if wintry conditions return, as they usually do, the brakes are quickly applied.

2

FEBRUARY

Watching birds and waiting for insects

The calendar reassures me that February is a short month, but it seems long, the very nadir of winter. In some years, spring seems to be on the way, and lured outside by watery sunshine that looks deceptively warm from the security of the house, my spirits are raised by the promise embodied in the shiny, fat, red leaf buds of peonies, thrusting determinedly through the cold soil – an auspicious sight, for peonies are named after Paeon, the physician of the Greek gods. In medieval times they were an emblem of health, and even twentieth-century herbals recommend an infusion of powdered roots for treating nervous disorders. Equally cheering are the slender new shoots surrounding last year's dead tarragon stalks; our name for it is a corruption of *esdragon* (French), and it is deemed one of the 'dragon' herbs believed to be efficacious in curing bites and stings of 'venomous beasts', even the bites of mad dogs. Peony and tarragon between them guarantee ample protection for the rigours of the coming season, and their early appearance augurs well. Yet, to be honest, my tarragon is something of a mistake, purchased on the assumption that it was the French variety whose leaves add an agreeably tart flavour to chicken stuffing and gravy, but proving to be the less aromatic Russian variety, which I find of little culinary use, although the plant adds variety to the garden flora, and insects like the flowers.

Although not immediately obvious, there are always some moth caterpillars to be found, although not the hairy sort first called caterpillars in the fifteenth century, supposedly because they resembled little hairy (*pilosa* in Latin) cats. Ignore the finger-numbing cold, delve deep among the rock-garden plants, turn over the basal leaves of foxgloves and forget-me-nots, and shake the sprawling growth of spotted dead-nettle. The usual rewards are green or brown, plaited-looking caterpillars of the angle shades, and the more robust, brownish ones of the lesser yellow underwing, but I also have winter feeding records of the caterpillars of the setaceous Hebrew character on foxglove, the yellow shell on marjoram, *Arabis* and *Aubretia*, the common marbled carpet on saxifrage, and the winter moth on shrubby cinquefoil. Caterpillars of the angle shades, in particular, can be found in any month of the year. They are extremely catholic in their choice of food and so, whatever the season, find food in gardens, where herbaceous and rock plants retain green leaves throughout the year.

The collectors who first described the English moths have left us a fascinating legacy of vernacular names for them, often descriptive, frequently pleasing, sometimes erudite, and occasionally baffling. The lesser yellow underwing is dowdy at rest with the wings folded flat along the back, and scuttles around on the ground like a little brown mouse, but in flight it reveals golden yellow hind wings. The setaceous Hebrew character, like many moths, bears marks on its fore wings that can be likened to characters in various sorts of script; 'setaceous' means bristle-like, but may be a mis-spelling of cetaceous (whale-like), refer- ring either to the shape of marks on the wings or to their oily sheen. The marbled carpet rests with its marbled wings closely pressed against the surface on which it has settled, the winter moth flies only in winter, and the wings of the yellow shell, though variable in colour and often more brown than yellow, are marked with delicate, curving lines centred on the wing base, reminiscent of the growth lines on a bivalve sea shell. The fore wings of the angle shades are delicately patterned in pinky-buff and moss-green, and it rests with them folded over the body and hind wings. Rather than lying flat, the wings form a tuck where they meet in the midline, and are infolded along their length so that the serrated margin appears deeply indented at the back. This posture, and a curious double tuft of prominent scales on the back give it a markedly angular appear- ance.

The problem of names

I have mentioned a few of the garden moths, those whose caterpillars may be encountered in February, but the names of others read like the cast list for a midsummer's eve masque, and anyone but an English moth-hunter would be puzzled as to the subject of a complete catalogue: the sallow kitten, the coxcomb prominent, the common footman, the peach-blossom, the Chinese character, the lackey, the powdered quak- er, the shark, the miller, the old lady, the brown rustic, the uncertain, the gold spangle, the herald, the snout, the streamer, the July highflyer, the chimney-sweeper, the seraphim, the pale brindled beauty, the ghost, the leopard, and many more.

Distinctive though these names are, they are endemic to the British Isles, neither recognizable nor understandable to a foreign lepidopterist, and they could be applied differently in other English-speaking countries. For international communication, and accuracy, it is necessary to use scientific names, which employ Latin words or latinized forms of words derived from other languages. The Latin names of plants and animals are a universal language immediately intelligible and meaningful to Germans, Russians, Japanese or whoever. All plants and animals are designated by a binomial, i.e. by two Latin names, the first of which is the name of a genus (plural: genera) or small group of similar organisms, and the second of which is particular to one kind or species within that group. The lesser yellow underwing is *Noctua comes*; there are other species of *Noctua*, but only one bears the name *comes*. Generic names are correctly applied to only one genus of organisms, whereas a specific name may be used in association with different generic names. Thus, the binomial, made up of generic and specific names, is unique to one species of animal or plant. Many small, inconspicuous plants and animals, especially those hard to distinguish from other species, have no vernacular names, and for these we have no choice but to use scientific names. It is convention to print the names in italics, as when words are borrowed from other languages, with a capital letter to start the generic name, and if this is observed there can be no doubt as to the meaning of a name used in isolation. When a generic name is obvious from the context, it is customary to abbreviate it to its initial letter when naming species, so that *Noctua comes* may be designated as *N. comes*.

We owe the sensible and neat binomial system of nomenclature to the eighteenth-century Swedish botanist, Linnaeus, whose invention happily disposed of the tedious necessity of designating particular plants or animals with a lengthy description – in Latin of course. Linnaeus also devised a practical classification of living organisms, in which degrees of similarity were used to construct a hierarchy. Linnaeus's classification has been revised considerably in the light of subsequent acceptance of evolution and recognition of differing degrees of relationship between organisms, and there are now more categories than he recognized, but the system used today is essentially the same as that he devised. Similar species are grouped in a genus, similar genera in a family, families in orders, and so on through classes and phyla (singular: phylum) to the broad division between the animal and plant kingdoms; the same general principles apply to the classification and nomenclature of micro-organisms. Thus the genus *Noctua* is part of the family Noctuidae, which together with all other moth and butterfly families constitutes the order Lepidoptera; this is grouped with all other insect orders, such as Coleoptera (beetles) and Diptera (flies), in the class Insecta; insects, together with crustaceans, spiders, centipedes and a number of other types of animal that have an external skeleton and jointed legs, constitute the phylum Arthropoda, one of twenty-two phyla generally recognized today within the animal kingdom.

Barriers to breeding

Classification can be controversial, and specialists do not always agree on degrees of similarity or closeness of relationship between different organisms, but the concept of a species is much more clearly defined. The members of a species are actually or potentially able to breed with each other, and in normal circumstances (in the wild) do not breed with members of other species. In captivity or under domestication, where conditions are far from normal, they may do so, but the resulting offspring are usually sterile. Obviously, when the geographical range of a species is large, as in the kestrel or hawthorn, individuals from one part of the range have no contact with those hundreds of miles away, but as long as breeding is continuous throughout the range, then the entire species is connected by reproduction.

What happens when range is not continuous? In North America there is a camouflaged moth very similar to the peppered moth (*Biston betularia*) that rests by day on tree trunks in Britain, but they are isolated from each other by the Atlantic Ocean, and there is no possibility of one breeding with the other. On the basis of consistent differences in appearance, they are designated as different species, although no-one knows for sure. When an insurmountable physical barrier, such as an ocean, divides the range of a species into two, each group is likely to be exposed to different environmental conditions. Within each group, those individuals best fitted to meet the demands of their particular environment are most likely to survive and reproduce, and hence make a greater contribution to the next generation than those less well able to cope. Since most differences between individuals are inherited, each group gradually becomes adapted to its surroundings by a process of natural selection or 'survival of the fittest'. Over many generations, the two groups may also accumulate sufficient fortuitous inherited differences in behaviour and structure, such that, in the event of removal of the barrier, they are physically unable to interbreed, and may not even recognize each other as 'like'. This is how species are formed: they evolve gradually from isolated populations (breeding groups) of other species.

All the familiar kinds of garden animals are good species, unable to interbreed, although it may take an expert to distinguish with confidence different species of slugs, earthworms, woodlice and many other groups. The situation with plants, however, is rather less clear-cut, for a number of reasons. First, many plants propagate themselves vegetatively, from arching stems that root at the tip (blackberries), runners (strawberries), lateral roots (raspberries), rhizomes or underground stems (some irises), bulbs (daffodils), or corms (crocuses), producing a potentially infinite number of new plants which are identical simply because they are offshoots of the parent, with little individuality. Secondly, any desirable feature that arises spontaneously in a plant may be seized on by horticulturalists who can produce vast numbers of plants either by exploiting natural vegetative propagation or by grafting and cuttings. This is true of many varieties of fruits grown in gardens. Vast numbers of apple trees or raspberry plants are really bits of the same individual, and the breeding criteria for deciding on the number of species rarely exist. Thirdly, horticulturalists have produced hybrids by artificially cross-pollinating different species. A whole range of garden cultivars, including Russian comfrey, border pinks, montbretia and some ornamental *Prunus*, are in this category, and this is why most fail to set seed. Finally, flowers and vegetables have been subject to the same intense and diversifying artificial selection as have dogs. The wild cabbage (*Brassica oleracea*) that grows on cliff tops in southeastern England is a tough-leaved, unpalatable, loose-headed plant, but from it have been bred an astonishing range of vegetables, from tight-hearted cabbages to Brussels sprouts, broccoli and cauliflowers, strikingly different from the parent plant and each other, yet all the same species. Roses, tulips, daffodils, and a number of other garden favourites have been subject to the same diversifying selection, and, as with pedigree dogs, rigorous control of who breeds with whom is required for there to be any chance of replicating the parent in the offspring, rather than producing an undistinguished 'mongrel'. Gardens are full of horticultural varieties, or cultivars, whose replication depends on the gardener's interference or control, and to add to the confusion, many have been given distinctive names, not only in English, but often in Latin. Commercial rose-growers have probably contributed most to the proliferation of names, christening every variety of floribunda and tea rose – which are hybrids anyway. This is not to say that it is impossible to make a list of plant species in a garden. After all, some garden flowers are unmodified wild species, but when it comes to cultivars, caution and some knowledge of their origins are called for.

Safety in numbers

We can now return to the quest for animals in the February garden armed with a more precise language in which to describe what we find. Apart from caterpillars in the rockery, there are numerous other invertebrates to be found sheltering in nooks and crannies, among them woodlice. Why is it that, winter or summer, woodlice have to be sought beneath stones or in crevices, and why is it more usual to find a huddle of them rather than a solitary woodlouse? The answer to these questions lies in their susceptibility to desiccation, which has resulted in the evolution of behaviour that tends to keep them in humid situations. But first, why are they so prone to water loss, in comparison, for instance, with insects?

They are terrestrial representatives of an aquatic group of animals, the class Crustacea, which includes shrimps, crabs and lobsters. Although enclosed by an external skeleton like that of shrimps, woodlice lack the waxy, waterproof cuticle layer that has fitted insects so successfully for the dry rigours of life on land; the cuticle is porous, and they are prone to lose water over the entire surface. Furthermore, like their aquatic relatives, they acquire oxygen for respiration using gills, situated on the underside of the abdomen, but gills have to be kept moist so that dissolved oxygen can diffuse into the blood system, and this increases the risk of water loss. In those species most tolerant of dry environments, the gills are enclosed by a flap which bears a system of air channels opening to the outside by a small pore and confers some protection against water loss from the gill surfaces. Nevertheless, the system for oxygen acquisition is essentially one appropriate for use in an aquatic medium. On land it causes problems – unless a woodlouse remains in relatively humid air. How does it do this?

Using a simple experimental set-up consisting of two adjoining compartments, it is possible to present woodlice with a choice between extremes in one condition (say temperature) while others are kept uniform throughout. In dry, or warm, or light situations they move rapidly and randomly, but they become still and hence congregate in moist, or cool, or dark situations. Moreover, they respond positively to bodily contact, moving rapidly in exposed situations, but becoming still when confined, whether in a crevice or surrounded by other woodlice. On balance, cool, dark, confined places are likely also to be humid, and huddling together reduces the surface area of each that is exposed to the drying effect of air. Thus, several aspects of woodlouse behaviour can be interpreted as adaptations for maintaining a humid environment, where water loss will be at a minimum. And this is why woodlice (and rarely a woodlouse) are to be found under stones.

There are at least three species of typical flattened woodlice in my garden, all common and widespread throughout Britain, and one species of pill-bug, *Armadillidium vulgare*, which on being disturbed rolls up with its back, which is covered with protective plates, outwards – like a miniature armadillo. Pill-bugs in general are found chiefly on chalky soils, where they can assimilate the quantities of calcium necessary for formation of their massive armour, but *A.vulgare* has exploited the enrichment of soils with calcium caused by building (and demolition) activities, and is fairly widespread, although local in the north and west of England, rare in Scotland and absent from northwest Ireland. Overall, the distribution of woodlice is determined not only by availability of calcium, but also by climate, especially by humidity and temperature. Different species differ in the exact range of their tolerance and so have different geographical distributions.

In a garden such as mine, with dense vegetation and an abundance of dead plant material, not just concentrated in the compost heap, but distributed over the soil, there is abundant food for woodlice. They are generally decomposers, feeding on dead plant material, and to a lesser extent on animal remains and faeces, although some species eat seedling plants, and in California, where it has been introduced, *A.vulgare* is a predator of the larvae and pupae of fruitflies (*Drosophila*). Woodlice also eat their own faeces, and indeed die when prevented from doing so. This appears to be because they need to maintain large reserves of copper (a component of the respiratory pigment in their blood). Much of the copper ingested in their food is bound up in complex compounds that are not broken down in the gut, and so are lost in the faeces. Bacterial activity in faeces, however, changes copper into a form that woodlice can use, and so, to acquire the essential copper, they must pass food through the gut twice. This habit is parallel to that of rabbits, which eat soft droppings voided at night, and so derive benefit from the digestive activities of bacteria living in the lower part of the alimentary canal where capacity for absorption of digestive products is limited.

An ambush at every corner

Sooner or later, while peering under stones searching for woodlice, spiders will be encountered, even in February when they tend to be inactive and inconspicuous because of low temperatures. All are formidable predators of other invertebrates (including spiders), but despite their ferocity they can ingest only liquid food. Many use sticky threads, often in the form of a web, to ensnare prey, which is immobilized by injection of poison from glands that open at the tip of sharp fangs mounted on grasping, jaw-like mouth appendages. A few species also inject enzymes into their prey, and eventually suck out the fluid products of digestion, but most crunch up their prey between a pair of appendages close to the mouth, mixing it with digestive enzymes, suck in the juices, and discard a mangled husk.

Beside the now empty pond in my garden is a stone-lined overflow shaft, topped by a flagstone, dark and damp, and a favourite haunt of woodlice. In one of the angles of the shaft is a lacy mesh of bluish-white cobweb: prod this gently with a twig, and the massive, shiny black head and jaws of a female *Amaurobius ferox* heave into view, followed by its robust, long-legged body. (This spider used to be called *Ciniflo ferox*, a much more spidery-sounding name!) Although only about 1.5 centimetres in length, its appearance so close, as I peer into the shaft on my hands and knees, is momentarily alarming. The strands of her loose web are adhesive, and she pounces quickly on any woodlouse that falls or blunders onto one of the sticky threads, immobilizes it, and hauls it into her lair. She leads a quiet life, on the whole, lying in wait for a woodlouse to trip into her web, and never needs stir far for food. Nor for sex, for, sooner or later, an errant male will find her. Their courtship consists essentially of appeasement on his part, to demonstrate that he is not food, and he stays no longer than is necessary. She lays a batch of eighty or more eggs in a crevice within her lair, and guards them until they hatch.

A close relative, *Amaurobius similis*, slightly smaller, has a lair in the outside wall of the house, between the backdoor jamb and the brickwork. She can be teased into pouncing from her retreat by vibrating a strand of her web. Female *Amaurobius* spiders extend or repair their webs little by little, a few strands each night, as befits year-round residents, in contrast to garden spiders, who are very much 'summer people', and construct their beautiful but insecure orb-webs quickly, in one working shift. Simple though an *Amaurobius* web is, the building materials are complex. As four delicate strands of silk emerge from the spinnerets at the tip of the spider's abdomen, she combs them with special structures on her hind legs, working loops into two of them, and combining the complex 4-ply strand with ribbons of sticky glandular secretion, to produce a lacy, adhesive thread. It ends up a bit like that very fancy knitting yarn which has several strands of differing textures, one or two of them looped and zig-zagged across the others. This is the type of cobweb that I tend to brush energetically away in efforts to 'tidy up', and the sticky threads ball up and become themselves ensnared in the bristles of the brush.

Removing cobwebs removes temporarily spiders' means of catching food, and may indeed be hastening the decline in numbers of some species which are suffering from our twentieth-century obsession with cleanliness. Among the prime targets of spring-cleaning are the hammock-shaped webs of house spiders (*Tegenaria domestica*). Other species of *Tegenaria* and the very similar *Textrix* (same family) construct hammock-shaped webs in the garden. *T.domestica* is the long-legged, fast-moving spider whose appearance in the bath or on the floor strikes terror into the faint-hearted. Males are easily recognized, because the palps, a pair of appendages just anterior to the front legs, end in shiny bulbous structures, and are held up as the spider runs along. During mating, the palps are used to insert sperm, stored in the bulbous palpal organs, into the female. Keeping her 'at arms length', even during copulation, is not such a bad idea when you consider that in all spiders the male has to work hard to overcome the female's inclination to treat him as food.

Inequality of the sexes

Female spiders seem positively emancipated in comparison with the females of many of the species of moth that fly in winter. Not that there are many. Night after February night, the light trap is run to no avail. Persistence eventually has some rewards, although few individuals are caught, and there is little variety. A pale brindled beauty, its greyish wings sparsely patterned with darker speckles and lines, may be the only capture, and, moreover, only males are trapped. Why is this? A curious feature of winter-flying moth species is the high proportion in which the adult female is wingless or effectively so, looking nothing like a moth, but more like a large aphid or frog-hopper. Their lives are short and uneventful from the time they emerge from pupae in leaf litter and soil beneath the deciduous trees or shrubs on which they feed as caterpillars. They clamber laboriously up the trunk, where the winged males find them, lay eggs and then die.

There are advantages in winter-flying moths having wingless females. When both males and females fly, at least two searching flights have to be accomplished: first the male has to find a female, and then the female has to find a foodplant. Moreover, if virgin females fly, it may take longer for males to find them. At a season when low temperatures, wind, freezing rain, or snow make flying hazardous, it is obviously efficient to reduce the number of flights to a minimum. The simplest way of achieving this, and at the same time guaranteeing that eggs are laid on an appropriate foodplant, is for the female to be wingless. She never leaves the plant on which she spent her life as a caterpillar, merely crawling down prior to pupation, and clambering up after emergence as an adult, to lay eggs on what is bound to be the correct foodplant. The eggs hatch into caterpillars in spring or early summer, when leaves first break from the bud. New leaves are softer and more palatable than older leaves, and it is to take advantage of this that caterpillars are produced so early in the year. Inevitably this has led to adults emerging in winter, but the hazards of winter flight are kept to a minumum because females are wingless.

The story of the holly leaf-miner

One common and widespread species of leaf-eating insect is around as a larva in February, but only the results of its feeding activities are visible, not the insect itself. Outside my study window are four large holly trees, many of whose glossy, green leaves are disfigured by irregularly shaped yellowish-brown blotches. A number of small holly trees that have established themselves elsewhere in the garden are similarly affected, even though they have relatively few leaves. On a walk around the neighbourhood, it is impossible to find a holly in parks or gardens without these leaf blotches. Closer inspection shows that the blotches are slightly puffy, as though a blister had formed beneath the leaf surface. These are feeding excavations of holly leaf-miners, the larvae of an undistinguished little fly, *Phytomyza ilicis*.

The adult flies can often be seen flying and walking around holly leaves in June, when females lay eggs at the base of the midrib of the leaves. The eggs soon hatch, and each minute larva (usually only one to a leaf) begins to eat its way along the tissues of the midrib, until in late autumn or early winter it moves out into the leafblade. Here it continues chewing away at the soft green tissue beneath the upper leaf surface, forming an irregular mine which reaches its maximum size in March. By this time the larva is fully grown and about three millimetres long; it prepares a thin, triangular area on the upper leaf surface against which it pupates. In late May, an adult fly emerges, leaving an irregularly-shaped hole or flap on the leaf surface.

There is little doubt that many plant structures (such as prickles) and much of the chemistry of plants (such as tannins and other poisons) have been evolved as deterrents to herbivores, and the orthodox view of herbivorous insects is that they are 'bad' for plants. However, investigation of the fate of mined holly leaves sheds a rather different light on plant-insect relationships. Holly trees produce new leaves in June, and individual leaves may remain on the tree for as long as four years. June-July is the period of maximum leaf fall, although some leaves fall in late summer and autumn. By placing white plastic trays beneath the holly trees in the garden, periodically emptying them, and counting mined or unmined leaves, it was possible to show that some mined leaves fall at all times of year, but that in the period January-May, almost all falling leaves are mined. One effect of holly leaf-miners is thus to cause more evenly spaced leaf fall. Once a leaf falls, the softening action of rain and the feeding activities of decomposers release the nutrients it contains into the soil, where they are available for absorption through the tree's roots. The holly's response to leaf-miners means that nutrients are recycled and redistributed through the tree at all times of year, rather than for a limited season. Leaf-miners may therefore be advantageous to the tree, and it certainly cannot be assumed that the tree suffers by their presence.

Mining a leaf might seem a safe and secure way of acquiring food; certainly there is no danger of food shortage – as long as the holly tree retains the leaf –, but the larvae are not safe from attack by specialized parasites and predators. At least nine different species of tiny parasitic wasps probe mines with their ovipositors, some species laying their eggs in larvae, others in pupae. The developing wasp larva gradually consumes the fly larva or pupa, and eventually a wasp, rather than a fly, emerges from the mine by a small, circular hole. One of these wasp species behaves as a secondary parasite in summer, laying eggs in mines already containing parasitic wasp larvae of other species. As a further complication, predators of holly leaf-miners eat parasitized and unparasitized fly larvae indiscriminately.

One of the best-loved and most familiar garden birds, the blue tit, is an efficient predator of holly leaf-miners, especially in late winter when the larvae are fully grown. Blue tits stab with their beaks at mines in holly leaves, and if they are able to pierce the shiny leaf surface, lever it up and extract the larva from beneath, leaving a V-shaped tear. These tears are easily recognizable, and so the success with which blue tits feed on holly leaf-miners can be investigated. Two of the large trees in my garden differ markedly in prickliness, one having an average of 9.4 prickles per leaf, the other only 1.4. By sampling leaves on the two trees and scoring for intact mines and those opened by blue tits, it became evident that the birds are about twice as successful in extracting larvae from the leaves of the less prickly tree. Imagine the manoeuvring necessary to gain a firm stance on a shiny holly leaf amid a tangle of prickles, and this seems very reasonable.

Opportunism in birds

Blue tits are supreme opportunists and have been able to turn adroitness acquired by such feeding strategies as extracting holly leaf-miners from tough, smooth-surfaced leaves, to exploitation of a very different source of nourishment. They use their beaks to tear open cardboard milk-bottle tops and to hammer holes in foil ones. The habit of opening milk-bottles and drinking the cream is widespread among blue tits, and there are records of milk-stealing by a number of other species of birds, particularly great tits. It first began to be noticed in the 1920s, but the habit spread rapidly and now occurs in most parts of the country. Although tits undoubtedly learn by copying each other, initial outbreaks of the habit are so widely scattered that it appears to have been independently acquired many times. The rewards of extending normal feeding movements to this new food source are such that the habit would be quickly learnt. There are no obvious rewards for other annoying habits of tits such as paper-tearing, when they damage wallpaper, books, lampshades and many other articles, and pecking putty from window frames. They tend to show this unusual behaviour when population density is high and food is scarce, and it often precedes or accompanies mass migrations. The pecking and tearing movements involved are again similar to food-searching behaviour, and also show some similarities to the activities of enlarging entrances to nest-holes and collecting nesting material. Day after day, I watched, from my kitchen window, the valiant attempts of a blue tit to enlarge a slit near the top of the metal foulstack on the nextdoor house. Rusty though the metal appeared to be, the blue tit made little impression on it, but persevered. Birds that engage in such persistent yet fruitless behaviour may be especially prone to indulge in apparent vandalism of wallpaper, cardboard boxes or window putty when under stress.

House sparrows search brittle dried sprays on a buddleia, that I forgot to prune, for any remaining seeds, and greenfinches are active in the February garden, picking seeds from compost spread over newly dug beds. Greenfinches, like blue tits, quickly learn new eating habits. They acquired a new food source in the early nineteenth century, when some individuals learned to eat daphne seeds while they are still soft in mid-summer, and the habit has spread at a rate of about three kilometres a year. In February, however, birds have to search diligently to find enough food, especially those that eat insects and other invertebrates. It must have been a real bonus for an opportunist robin when, on a cold February day, I decided that the dilapidated and rotting front gates would serve more usefully as firewood. The ever-watchful robin was soon searching busily along the dismantled timbers and through the wood fragments, presumably finding small spiders and other tasty morsels. The robin was not alone in searching the planks, for I discovered that the oak gates had been constructed using copper nails. With increasing demand for a limited supply, copper is now too expensive to be made into nails, whatever the advantages in endurance, and I have kept the nails as a memento of a time when supplies of raw materials seemed infinite.

One particularly cold February, when snow lay thick on the ground, the bouquets of swelling buds and leaves atop tall broccoli stems proved an irresistible attraction to three fat woodpigeons. The plants swayed and bent beneath their weight, but even a furious hand-clapping run up the garden failed to deter them for long, and I was left with mangled, skeletal plants, the leaves shredded down to the midribs. The plants unexpectedly recovered and the pigeons stayed away, and so I was eventually able to harvest the sweet flower buds.

Collared doves are ubiquitous in suburban gardens and advertise their presence so insistently from chimney-pots and television aerials, that it is hard to believe that they are recent immigrants to Britain. By the sixteenth century, they had spread from northern India to southeastern Europe, but extended their range no further until 1930. Then they spread rapidly across Europe, reaching Britain in 1955, and have continued to move northwest. At first they were protected, but in the space of 15 years numbers increased to between 15,000 and 25,000 breeding pairs, and now they are controlled by shooting. The rate of increase has slowed, but they have become an integral part of the suburban garden scene and sounds. Their rapid spread and explosive increase in numbers suggest that there were hitherto unexploited opportunities in suburbia for a small dove. They take advantage of scattered grain in and around chicken runs, and large flocks feed at spillages around grain stores, but in my experience they are gleaners of seeds in general, and find plenty to eat in a varied garden such as mine.

Spring beckons

In milder years, thrushes begin to sing, and the cool air seems to echo with the doleful call of collared doves. I cannot understand why people object to their repetitive notes, for it is a liquid, gentle sound. All over Africa, there are small doves with similar mournful calls, and for me their notes are evocative of warmer lands, and always welcome. Their early song is a prelude to the increased garden activity that I look forward to in March. Crocuses, snowdrops, forsythia and daphne brighten the bare garden; the pale flowers of Myrobalan plum spangle its purplish-brown twigs long before the surrounding trees show any sign of life; the grey-green cushions of *Aubretia* are enlivened by scattered purple flowers, and a warm spell has coaxed open a few daffodils. In particularly mild years, there is the bonus of an early buttercup, with its evocation of golden summer days ahead, and a few dark green strands of the cultivated broom, that droops over a corner of the lawn, become frosted with cool, cream-coloured flowers.

The day-dreams conjured up by seed catalogues are now revised into a semblance of reality by a serious effort to plan the coming year's planting programme. Having drawn a rough sketch of the garden lay-out, it again becomes evident how little space there is for annual flowers and vegetables and for additions to the permanent flora. Undaunted, I make a list of plants I want to grow from seed, and attempt on paper the puzzle of fitting them into the available space. I never gauge accurately just how much space each plant needs, and my garden sketch ends up looking like a detailed mosaic. One reason for this is my preference for mixed plantings, not just of flowers, but also of vegetables with flowers. I like the contrasting patchwork of colour and shades of green, of leaf shape and plant form that this produces, and actively dislike straight rows and geometric precision in a garden. Furthermore, the probabilities of particular sorts of insects increasing in numbers and getting out of hand as pests, are reduced by avoiding concentrations of one sort of plant. A gaudy splash of marigolds shows to advantage against the dull blue-green of cabbages, the silvery-white flowers of nicotiana add fragrance and delicacy to the vegetable patch, and a variety of insects, including potential predators of pests, are summoned to the mixed bed of lettuce, radishes, cabbages and beans by the yellow-centred, royal blue trumpets of dwarf convolvulus. I entertain the possibilities of growing different flowers to attract insects to the garden. Many horticultural varieties are of little use as food to nectar- or pollen-feeding butterflies, moths, bees and flies because the close cluster of petals in a 'double' flower both hides and blocks access to nectaries or pollen-bearing stamens. So I decide to try *Lavatera*, a member of the mallow family which bears rosy-pink hollyhock-like flowers, deep blue viper's bugloss which should tempt bees, and a bright yellow black-eyed Susan (*Rudbeckia*), whose flat, composite flowers should attract and satisfy hoverflies. Cheered by an image of how the garden should look in a few months' time – after some hard work – I feel that spring is on the way, and, as February draws to a close, the end of winter is in sight.

3

MARCH

First butterflies

The weather in March varies so much from year to year, that no gardener can say with confidence 'This is the time to sow seeds', or naturalist claim 'This is when butterflies appear and birds start nesting'. Although the actual sequence of events is much the same from one spring to the next, the growth of plants and activities of animals cannot be rigidly matched to the calendar. In this small island, exposed on the one hand to wet westerlies, and on the other to the wind systems of a contintental land mass, weather is as unpredictable as almost anywhere in the world. No wonder that it is such a pervasive topic of conversation. Departures from seasonally average temperature or rainfall seem to be the norm, hence the rueful claim that Britain has weather not climate. Spring is 'early' or 'late' in nearly every year, and so it is risky to assert positively what happens in the garden in March. Any statement would not hold good for more than one year in two or three. Perhaps this has improved the perception of British gardeners and nature-watchers, kept constantly on the alert, rarely able to lean back comfortably on habit or routine predictions. This may also be why, as gardeners, we tend to be optimists. If March is going to be warm, and the season well advanced, in one year out of two or three, then we happily gamble on it being this year.

In five of the ten years that I have been looking at this garden, wintry conditions have been so persistent that snow has fallen in April. In one year, extreme cold in February arrested the opening of daphne flowers, so that there were effectively two episodes of blossoming, one in January, and another in March. But we do tend to remember the good years – all childhood summers were blazingly hot, and it never rained – and a garden calendar that talked of snow in March as being usual would be dismissed as unduly pessimistic. So let us look on the bright side, and view the garden in March in an optimistic light. Snowdrops, crocuses and aconites are almost over, but the daphne persists, the dull green cushions of *Aubretia* sport more and more violet and magenta blooms, and the straggling mats of *Arabis* are highlighted by white flower clusters. The Myrobalan plum is in full flower, like a miniature galaxy against the evening sky, rosy-purple heath brightens the rockery, and canary-yellow *Mahonia* flowers contrast with its shiny, spiky leaves. The pendulent, pinky-red flower clusters of flowering currant waft in the breeze against tender green leaves, their pungent scent mingling with the strange perfume emanating from the pale froth of flowers on a hybrid broom.

Now is the time to have a determined onslaught against the ubiquitous marguerite daisy (*Chrysanthemum frutescens*) and wood avens – the first a cultivated alien, the second a native that came in of its own accord, but both behaving as vigorous weeds – while vegetation is low and sparse enough for me to get at them. It comes as a surprise to find so many holly seedlings. Holly is reputedly difficult to grow, but seeds scattered by birds, that have eaten the berries, sprout everywhere. I have a compulsive urge to tidy up and lick the garden into shape before the great summer burgeoning of vegetation, and furtively trim birch trees, beauty bush and drooping sprays of a hybrid spiraea, now it is evident that their new growth will swamp and shadow nearby plants. The garden looks good, bursting with new growth, but contained and definitely under control, at least for the time being.

Awakening insects

Spring sunshine and rising temperatures end the hibernation of those butterflies that have passed the winter as adults. This will not be a brief stretch of the wings, like a tortoiseshell's emergence in January sunshine, but the final end to winter sleep now that there are more flowers around at which they can refuel. A tortoiseshell suns itself on the stone path, and the yellow-ringed 'eyes' of a peacock stare unseeingly from the south-facing front wall of the house, where it basks with open wings. The veins of an insect wing, the struts that support the delicate sail, are filled with 'blood' that also slowly circulates around the muscles and internal organs. The sun shining on the expanded wings warms the 'blood' in the veins, and gradually the muscles, to a temperature at which sustained flight activity is possible. Butterflies tend to bask on south-facing walls, sometimes on the ground, orienting themselves so that the sun's rays fall at right angles to the plane of the wings, for the maximum heating effect.

Warmer days have caused other insects to stir from their winter sleep. Amid a blur of rapidly oscillating wings, a drone fly hovers in the sun, and another of these large hoverflies rests and feeds on a golden crocus. A honeybee inspects, one by one, the deep pink bells of winter-flowering heath in its quest for nectar and pollen to take back to the awakening hive. A furry, rufous-coloured flower or potter bee (*Anthophora*) zooms rapidly among the spotted dead-nettle flowers that carpet the raspberry patch, and I mistake it for the first bumblebee of the year. They are solitary, unlike the social bumblebees, and females construct little clay 'pots' in the ground. They fill each with pollen and honey, and lay an egg on top, before sealing it. Developing larvae feed on the stored food in their tiny earthen cells. Now a fat bumblebee, yellow-banded on black, meanders noisily into view – no mistake this time. It is an over-wintered queen, recognizable by her brownish tail as *Bombus terrestris*, about to start the task of rearing the year's first batch of worker bees. She is ponderous by comparison with the potter bee, and much larger, although it is easy to confuse the two in the first sightings of the year.

Butterflies and bees are not the only insects that have come out of hibernation. Ladybirds crawl from the bases of plants and from other nooks and crannies where they have sheltered for the last few months. This is more than the tentative emergence of 7-spots from the lavender cotton on sunny January days, for now they are fully active, and warm enough to fly. They always remind me of miniature flying machines, as they rise somewhat laboriously into the air, like old-fashioned bi-planes, holding the rigid wing cases (the front pair of wings) expanded in a shallow V behind the head. Like early planes, they lack manoeuvrability, and seem capable of only short flights from a good take-off point, unless they encounter a following wind. The most consistently abundant garden species is the 2-spot ladybird, usually red with two black spots, but sometimes black with red spots, or yellow with black spots. They are permanent residents, breeding in the garden, and passing the winter in hibernation, when they become dormant and completely inactive. The only ones seen in winter are those that have entered the house in autumn and have thus been kept unseasonally warm. In contrast, the larger 7-spot ladybirds, invariably red with seven black spots, only slow down when it is cold; they are active on any warm day, whatever the month, although it is not until March that they become warm enough to fly. 7-spots are not permanent residents, although for a number of consecutive years in the 1970s they bred and over-wintered in the garden.

Why cultivate grass?

Residents and visitors alike grumble that it is always raining in England. We become so obsessed by daily fluctuations in rainfall, either too much or too little, that we lose sight of its consistent moderation. Yet this is a 'green and pleasant land', whereas parts of the world, such as tropical West Africa, that get four times as much rain, are brown and parched for much of the year. The secret is that our rainfall is gentle, evenly distributed through the year, and usually accompanied by low temperatures. Consequently, neither vegetation nor topsoil are damaged by torrential downpours, the relatively small amount of rain that falls soaks evenly into the ground, and evaporation from the soil is low; in other words, the biological effectiveness of the rain is high. Cool, moist conditions without too much direct sun, are ideal for one feature of gardens for which England is justifiably famous – lawns. In few other parts of the world is it so easy to produce a velvety green-sward. The lawn needs attention, however, and now that rising temperatures have speeded up growth, it is time to get out the lawn-mower, flex the muscles, and give the grass its first trim of the year.

Gardeners strive manfully to establish grass even where climatic conditions are patently unsuitable, and lawns are a dominant feature of gardens wherever climate allows development of a good turf. They range from the formal lawns of grand gardens, and the park-like expanses favoured in much of Scandinavia and North America, to the trim, neat squares or rectangles characteristic of English suburban gardens. Some of the latter are large enough for children to play, sometimes even accommodating ball games and bike-riding, and many are used for sitting and eating outside, but a significant number are too small, too inconveniently sited, or too fussily maintained ever to be used for anything. What are they there for? Why have a lawn at all?

I think that domestic lawns have become a tradition, their maintenance has been ritualized, and the original reasons for establishing them have been forgotten. An historical reason for having open, grassy expanses round your dwelling place could be that you can see who is approaching, and presumably whether they are friend or foe. The more open your surroundings, the less likely you are to be taken by surprise. Furthermore, in times of intrigue, plot and counter-plot, there might be advantages in having somewhere to talk where you cannot be overheard; in this respect, a spacious lawn is far more secure than shaded walks or even the seclusion of the house, where eavesdroppers may lurk unseen. Ironically, with modern electronic surveillance methods, the same is true today. In more settled and self-conscious times, what better way of publicizing surplus wealth than to be seen to own and manage land to no profitable purpose, even employing others to maintain and groom the grass? Although the lawn-mower was invented in 1831, it was another 100 years before powered machines were developed, and extensive lawns could only be maintained by exercising muscle power. An article on the invention in *The Gardener's Magazine*, extolling its efficiency, suggested that 'Country gentlemen may find in using the machine themselves, an amusing, healthy exercise.'

Landscape gardeners, the artists of the gardening world, were quick to see the aesthetic contribution that sweeping lawns and green walkways can make to the composition of a garden. Specimen trees, colourful flower beds, bits of sculpture, the house itself, can all be seen to advantage against a smooth carpet of grass. Well-maintained lawns were once a means of projecting an image of affluence, comfort and good taste, and even in comparatively small gardens established in the late nineteenth and early twentieth centuries, this may have been important. As, however, social and economic conditions changed, and more people took over management of their own gardens, lawns became a way of projecting an image of tidiness, order and skill. To some extent this applies to front gardens in general, especially the small plots so common in suburbia. They are the showcase in which the house-holder displays an image of himself that he wishes to convey to others. I feel that this is particularly true of the minute, tidy scraps of lawn that are so often a central feature of such gardens. They serve no useful purpose, are too small to have any aesthetic appeal, but are a clue to the attitudes of the owner. Such speculations should probably not be carried too far – I wonder, for instance, what the conversion of two tidy, matched front lawns to jungly herbaceous beds indicates about me? – but whatever the details of the story, lawns undoubtedly can be explained in terms of social influences.

Since so many lawns are pocket-sized and functionless, it is remarkable how much money and effort go into their upkeep. There is a considerable degree of consensus about what constitutes a good quality turf – that it should be composed only of grass, for one thing – and gardening columns in newspapers, programmes on radio and television, gardening journals, books, and countless advertisements brim over with advice, and instruction tantamount to orders, about how to treat your lawn. According to a recent government publication, there were 12,860,800 domestic lawns covering a total of 90,000 hectares in the

United Kingdom in 1974, and £24 million was spent on lawn-mowers and other machinery. If the costs of establishing a lawn, time spent in maintaining it, and outlay on tools, grass seed, fertilizers, pesticides and watering are taken into account, cultivating grass appears to be an expensive pastime.

Lawn-mowers as grazers

There is no *a priori* reason why a lawn should be composed of grass alone, since all that is required is firm, short, compact growth, which will withstand trampling and remain green. For this grass is ideal, which is why it is the plant usually used, although there are exceptions, such as chamomile lawns. Why is grass so superior a lawn plant? The secret lies in its mode of growth and response to cutting. Most good lawn grasses are tufted perennials which spread by means of underground stems that produce a high proportion of leafy shoots. The buds that lead to thickening of the tuft and that produce the spreading underground stems are developed at or below ground level, where they are protected from trampling and the action of the lawn-mower by the bases of old leaf sheaths and by the soil. Cutting the leaves prevents production of flowering stems, and stimulates development of buds into vegetative shoots. The growth zone of a grass leaf is right at the base, so that the tip is the oldest part. New growth from the base pushes up the entire blade, until the leaf is fully expanded, so that after the end is removed, it appears to be replaced. If you cut the worn end from a daisy or rose leaf, there is no growth replacement, because their mode of development is quite different. As you cut away worn ends of grass leaves by mowing, however, growth from below makes good what you have removed. Repeated mowing consequently improves grass quality, as well as promoting establishment of thick, dense turf.

The growth form of grasses might seem to be pre-adapted for use of lawn-mowers, but to understand why grasses grow as they do, we have to look at natural grasslands. These evolved at the same time in the geological past as the large grazing animals. The teeth, tongues, jaws and digestive systems of antelope, cattle, deer, horses and other grazers are adapted for cropping and processing grass as food; grasses are adapted to repeated cropping of the leafblades and trampling. Grass and grazers are interdependent, and neither could have evolved without the other. What has this to do with a suburban lawn? A lawn-mower behaves as a grazer, and the grass responds in much the same way. Repeated mowing promotes vegetative growth and prevents grasses flowering; it also discourages the establishment of other sorts of plants. An unmown lawn soon contains a mixture of colonists, including seedling trees, and, in time, successional changes in plant associations culminate in the climax vegetation typical of the area. In the same way, exclusion of grazers from natural grasslands is often followed by establishment of trees and development of scrub or woodland. Grazers keep grasslands at an early successional stage, so well-defined that it is sometimes called a grazing climax. A lawn-mower similarly maintains a lawn as a grazing climax.

Some plants that colonize English lawns can, however, co-exist with lawn-mowers, because of low, compact growth and short flowering stems. Even turf as meticulously maintained as that of Lord's cricket ground has annual meadow grass, clover and a few buttercups growing in the lush outfield – the wicket is a different matter altogether. I leave most of these invaders alone, liking to see the varied leaf shape, texture and hue they add to the lawn; they resist trampling and in no way detract from compact cover of the ground. Close inspection reveals a garden in miniature: moss-like leaves of buttonweed; feathery, aromatic fronds of yarrow, traditionally used to cure wounds and hence called soldier's woundwort or knight's milfoil; tiny, oval leaflets of bird's-foot-trefoil, sometimes called 'bacon-and-eggs' because of its yellow and red flowers; downy leaves and brown flowers of field wood-rush; lucky leaves of white clover; and greater plantain, daisies and dandelions. Homely though these plants are, their names are delightful; dandelion is a corruption of *dent-de-lion* (French), referring to the toothed leaves, and daisy comes from the poetic Old English, *daeges ēage*, or 'day's eye'. Dandelions, and occasionally plantains, I remove, for the spreading leaf rosettes disrupt the green-sward and tend to smother grass, but the rest I enjoy. Lawn perfectionists, however, remove them as weeds.

Grass at any price?
It could be argued that by removing 'weeds' the gardener maximizes the productivity of his lawn grasses. He ensures that available nutrients are incorporated into grass and that none is wasted on undesirable plants. But orthodox wisdom on lawn management involves a paradox. Repeated cutting promotes the growth of grass, i.e. increases production, yet lawn-clippings are usually deposited on the compost heap or elsewhere in the garden, and the nutrients they contain are permanently removed from the lawn itself. Similarly, dead grass and leaves that fall or blow onto a lawn are raked away and deposited elsewhere. One school of

thought holds that a 'thatch' of litter and grass-cuttings smothers the growing grass, encourages weeds, worms, woodlice, slugs and other 'pests', increases the incidence of worm casts, creates damp conditions in which moss thrives, and generally interferes with turf quality. This has become an issue in an extravagant advertising battle between the manufacturers of aircushion mowers and of cylinder mowers with grass boxes, since raking after using an aircushion mower collects only about a third of the grass-clippings. No case, other than purely cosmetic, can be made for discouraging earthworms in a lawn; their burrowing and casting activities aerate, drain, break down and turn over the soil, which must improve availability of nutrients and lead to healthier grass. More important, though, are the consequences of removing the nutrients in grass-clippings from the lawn. I have always left cut grass *in situ*, believing that the recycling of nutrients that ensues is the simplest way of promoting better growth. Support for this opinion has come from a detailed analysis of the management and productivity of a 110 square metre lawn in California, USA.

During the course of a year, 63 kilograms dry weight (after heating to remove water) of living and dead vegetation were removed from the Californian lawn by raking and mowing. It was calculated that this contained, in one form or another, 3,300 grams of nitrogen, 960 grams of phosphorus and 1,850 grams of potassium, all of which are essential for growth. Some compensation had to be made for this nutrient drain, and a healthy lawn was maintained by addition of nearly 14.5 kilograms of fertilizer and manure, equivalent to 1,720 grams of nitrogen, 430 grams of phosphorus and 860 grams of potassium. Thus, despite application of fertilizers in considerable quantities, there was a net deficit as a consequence of standard management practices. Nitrogen, phosphorus and potassium occur in commercial fertilizers and manure in forms that are readily usable by plants, whereas the nutrients in grass-cuttings and litter are largely unavailable in the short term. In the long term, however, regular fertilizer application is needed to match the slow release of nutrients from cuttings and litter through decomposition. I am now convinced that I am better advised to leave grass-cuttings and litter on the lawn, so that the nutrients they contain are slowly recycled to the growing grass. As long as the lawn is mown frequently, so that grass-cuttings are short, there is little risk of build-up of a smothering 'thatch', and regular mowing breaks up and disperses fallen leaves and worm casts. Where trees grow close to lawns, however, sodden mats of fallen leaves may accumulate in autumn and need removing if the grass is to survive. Fortunately, I do not have this problem, and this may be why I rarely find moss in my lawn.

Mowing, weeding and raking all involve expenditure of time and energy, and standard management practices entail expense and effort in putting nutrients back into a lawn. It is becoming clear that a lot goes into maintenance of a lawn. Financial cost is one measure of input; another is energy. Everything that is done to a lawn can be expressed in standard units such as Calories. (A Calorie, familiar to slimmers who watch the calorific content of their diet, is the amount of heat needed to raise the temperature of one kilogram of water by 1°C, and hence can be used as a unit of energy.) To get some idea of energy input to a lawn, we can return to the Californian study, although a Californian lawn differs from an English one, in that it requires regular watering. The owner of the Californian lawn recorded in detail for one year every aspect of energy use directed towards maintenance. This included manpower used in mowing, raking litter, weeding, watering, applying fertilizers and pesticides, re-seeding and so on, as well as petrol used to drive the mower, electricity used to pump water, energy used in manufacturing fertilizers and other chemicals, and the energy content of seeds sown. Keeping his lawn 'reasonably attractive' required 1,865 Calories per square metre per year. This significance of this figure became apparent when it was compared with the 715 Calories per square metre per year used to grow maize, which is intermediate in terms of energy subsidy required to produce a satisfactory crop. Maize growing occupies only about 40 per cent of the year, but if we compare it with lawn maintenance for a similar period, the energy input to the lawn is still slightly higher. In other words, for the same energy input, home gardeners could grow vegetables instead of maintaining a lawn. As fossil fuels and hence energy become scarce and expensive, and as the cost of vegetables rises, there may be good reason to view the lawn speculatively. Is that velvety green-sward really more desirable than fresh salads and vegetables? Lawns could once more become an ostentatious luxury.

Life in and on a lawn

A lawn is usually a discrete habitat within a garden. We make an effort to keep the edges sharp, and leave a gully between grass and flower beds. The characteristic lawn 'weeds' are rarely successful in establishing themselves elsewhere in a garden, and together with lawn grasses form an identifiable plant association. Add to these the many sorts of animals especially associated with lawns, and we have a recognizable community interconnected by feeding and other interactions. The Californian study identified man as by far the dominant animal in an intensively-managed lawn community. He acts as a herbivore, because he removes a significant proportion of the living grass, and as a scavenger, or decomposer, when he removes surface litter. Many other animals are present, however, and, in a minimally-managed lawn like mine, they are instrumental in transfer and recycling of energy and nutrients.

A few small, mobile animals may be found on grass-blades, such as one or two species of bugs and a number of sorts of grass-feeding moth caterpillars, and predators like spiders run across the ground. Many more animals live deep down, where they are cushioned from the effects of feet and the mower. The real activity is within the litter layer and in the soil beneath. To see this, you have to turn over a divot of turf or extract a core of turf and soil, neither of which is guaranteed to improve the appearance of the lawn, but you can infer the presence of a multitude of hidden animals, first by the rate of disappearance of grass-cuttings and litter, and secondly by the activities of birds.

Earthworms are one of the dominant decomposers in the lawn community, eating fragments of plant material, and often pulling leaves down into their burrows. Within the litter layer and deeper within the soil, a multitude of tiny wingless insects, nematode worms, protozoans, bacteria and fungi contribute to the breakdown of dead grass leaves and roots. Some relatively large insects feed on living grass roots, and it is in their quest for these that a flock of starlings alights to probe busily, leaving the lawn pitted with holes. The juiciest morsels they find are probably the fat, sluggish caterpillars of large yellow underwing moths, although other caterpillars are there too. I watched a crane-fly or daddy-long-legs, probing the lawn with her ovipositor one autumn, depositing her eggs deep in the turf. These hatch into leather-jackets, which feed on grass roots, another tasty meal for starlings and other birds.

Birds do especially well for food on lawns. Their feeding efficiency is high, and they can extract far more food than from an equivalent area of natural grassland. The main reason for this is that a lawn is completely exposed, so that they can see any approaching danger, such as a cat; since lawn edges are usually sharply delimited, they can feed right up to the edge without risk. Furthermore, the shortness of the grass means that they have little difficulty locating and extracting worms, especially after rain or when grass is damp early in the morning, for then worms tend to move towards or actually onto the surface. In dry weather, worms burrow deep, seeking moist soil, and then blackbirds, thrushes and other worm-eating birds have more difficulty acquiring enough to eat. Since lawns are often watered in dry weather, they remain attractive and productive feeding grounds, and in outer suburbs, rooks may visit gardens to exploit good feeding conditions when pastures and fields are hard and dry.

Starlings are busy, noisy and quarrelsome, when they descend onto my lawn in a flock to search for insects and worms, but their visits are intermittent. Other birds are on the lawn whenever I glance outside, but make less fuss about feeding. A drab female blackbird hops along in leisurely fashion with head tilted to one side, pausing every so often to peck up a small food item. A black male joins her and chases a rival, with shrill, scolding calls. This male seems to have been around for some time, and has been responsible for many nests and broods, not all of which have successfully fledged. He has a distinctly down-at-heel appearance; his dark plumage is dull and slightly untidy, and one or two feathers on his head refuse to lie flat. By comparison, the speckled song thrush is dapper and jaunty. He hops a short distance, quickly inspects the ground, grabs and swallows a worm, and then momentarily pulls himself erect and slim, before continuing his foray. Blackbirds and thrushes are the real exploiters of lawns, quietly and persistently, all the year round, and in towns and suburbs they are largely dependent on lawns for food.

Other birds come and go from the lawn, also evidently finding something to eat. A pair of mousy hedge sparrows dart here and there, foraging intently for tiny spiders, insects and seeds, shivering their wings slightly as they hop about. In the evening sunlight, a pair of collared doves, their small heads elegantly poised on their plump shoulders, stroll to and fro, pausing every so often, and rather incongruously up-ending, like dabbling ducks, to peck up a few seeds. I often throw stale bread or other scraps onto the lawn to sustain birds in winter when the ground is hard, and two unexpected visitors, a mallard drake and duck, walk through the front gate, pass the kitchen window, jump floppily up the steps to the lawn, and greedily take the larger crusts. They probably come from the brook, 125 metres away across a busy road, for 400 metres downstream is a public park with resident bread-dependent mallard. Nevertheless, they take me by surprise, for they look so big on my small lawn, and I smile at the casual, neighbourly way they stroll in, rather than avoiding traffic by flying across the road.

The nesting season

One day early in March, I was idly inspecting my front garden to see how it was growing, when a colourful mallard drake walked in through the front gate as briskly as his waddle would allow. Ignoring me, he crossed the flower bed, all the time giving soft, hoarse quacks. I then saw a duck, pacing to and fro, behind the fence, in the nextdoor garden. Eventually her brown head appeared round the gate post, and she hesitantly followed the drake into the garden. Quacking quietly yet persistently, as though exhorting the duck to follow, the drake led her beneath the dense shrubbery at the side of the garden, where he settled, with a great plumping up of feathers, on the ground. It looked as though he were demonstrating that this would be a good place to nest, but she refused to settle, wandering around and pecking desultorily at the ground in the flower bed. I left them to sort out their problems, and half an hour later when I returned, they had gone. I hope they found a more secluded place to nest, where the ducklings would have no need to brave a busy road.

There is much other evidence of nesting in the garden. A blackbird diligently collects litter and straw from the surface of flower beds, and greenfinches carrying nesting material flit busily in and out of the dense mass of mock orange by the front door. The collared doves make repeated flights from the ground up into an adjacent Lawson's cypress, where they are building an untidy nest on a major branch, close to the trunk. They look delicate and agile as they fly straight up with inclined head, sharply angled wings and flared tail, more like terns than doves. For a couple of days I have the pleasure of watching their grace and elegance, then the nest is complete. I sometimes see one of them perching comfortably on an apple bough, pink in the evening sun, or calling gently from a chimney-pot, occasionally sounding almost like a cuckoo. Starlings are resident in the neighbourhood, and on every sunny March day, a glossy, full-throated male sings brashly from a perch high on the apple tree or a chimney-pot; I say 'sings', but his varied repertoire is a veritable babel of noises, including a very passable imitation of a 'trim-phone' ring, which has sent me running towards the house on more than one occasion. A male redpoll in full breeding dress, his red pate like a crude daub of bright paint, pecks seeds from cracks in the path. Redpolls, which feed mainly on birch seeds, have increased in numbers in the last thirty-five to forty years, and now breed in many areas to which they were previously only winter visitors. Thrushes are building deep in the shrubbery, great tits and blue tits are collecting nesting material, and pairs of robins and hedge sparrows give every indication of having nests somewhere nearby.

The architectural prize must go to a wren which constructed an enormous inter-woven nest mass of montbretia leaves, saxifrage clumps and dead grass, wedged behind honeysuckle against a fence. The loosely-constructed nest was based on a stout, thorny rose branch wired to the fence, and honeysuckle strands were woven into its fabric, so that it was rigidly held in place. The most delightful part of the construction was its decoration, for the moss fragments covering the outside were studded with mauve *Aubretia* flowers. Male wrens build several nests, only one of which is used, and this one was never occupied, although three days later it was redecorated with fresh flowers. The structure was not wasted, however, for a blackbird hollowed a smooth nest cup into the top of the mass, and laid three eggs. Two or three pairs of blackbirds breed in the garden, and the first eggs are usually laid in March.

Birds that start nesting in March feed on the ground on worms and other invertebrates, or on caterpillars on trees, and their breeding is timed so that young are in the nest at a season when the parents can readily collect enough food for them. But the actual onset of nesting can be adjusted, in the short term, in response to temperature. A cold spring that slows down plant growth, and insect development and activity, also delays nesting and egg-laying. Blackbirds desert their nests if it turns cold, although they may start nesting again within four days of the return of warmer weather. They raise several broods in a season, and breeding goes on for as long as soil is moist and worms readily available, although it may stop unusually early if the ground is dry and food scarce.

The tame male blackbird who keeps figuring in my descriptions of the garden daily searches the kitchen drain for fragments of rice, spaghetti, vegetables, anything tiny that has washed down the waste-pipe from the kitchen sink (and is no doubt conveniently softened by the hot water). His assiduous visits and unconcern at my approach suggest that this is a profitable source of food. Such opportunism is one of the many features of blackbirds that have enabled them to adapt successfully to gardens, although they are really woodland birds. Not only is the population density higher in gardens, but their breeding success is greater. In woodland around Oxford, for instance, there is about one pair to every two and a half hectares, and woodland blackbirds move around a lot, seeking seasonally available food, but in Oxford gardens there are seven or eight pairs to the hectare, and they are much more sedentary. In towns, each pair raises an average of 3.5 fledged young a year, but 40 per

cent of the adults die every year, and most of the young do not survive to
the next breeding season. I sometimes come across small, weak
fledglings on the lawn or path, and it is easy to assume that they have
been abandoned. But they should be left alone, for the parents will
return with food, and attempts to move the baby birds, or even take them
indoors, only ensure their death. The parents continue feeding the
young for some time after they leave the nest, and there always seem to
be a few demanding, but fully grown, youngsters around later in the
year, who persist in crouching, fluttering and plaintively squeaking like
babies, leading their harassed parents a merry dance.

Looking ahead

The nesting activities of blackbirds, thrushes, collared doves and other
garden birds are not the only indications that the season is under way.
Many more flowers appear. The clear purple spires of honesty stand tall
over the sprawling growth of spotted dead-nettle with its mauve or white
hooded flowers, and the first forget-me-nots, like fragments scattered
from a blue sky, look ethereal beside the stolid, fleshy growth of
multi-coloured primulas. The earliest varieties of *Narcissus* are now in
fat bud, and I pick them to take indoors, where they soon unfurl their
golden trumpets. A male brimstone butterfly, yellow as his name, sails
into view. He could be mistaken for a flower tossed by the wind, but
suddenly changes direction to settle on a primrose in the rockery. The
predilection of brimstones for yellow primroses is one of those happy
coincidences. There is no suggestion of a casual connection between
their colours, but it makes a pleasing picture as a yellow butterfly probes
a yellow flower for nectar amidst a cluster of crinkly green leaves.
Butterfly and plant are both woodland species, and primroses are
brimstones' main source of food.

Brimstones, like peacocks and tortoiseshells have over-wintered as
adults, but now a butterfly with a different life history appears in the
garden – a solitary small cabbage white, flapping its frail flight towards
the *Arabis* and *Aubretia* flowers. It seems delicate and fragile beside the
over-wintered butterflies, and unlike them is newly emerged as an adult.
All winter it has been a quiescent pupa hidden beneath a window-sill or
in some nook on fence or wall, while the massive reorganization needed
to form a butterfly from a caterpillar has been proceeding. Early summer

PLATE 3   5 Sweet pea and bean trellises are in place in the lawn bed by
mid-May, but little is growing, apart from rows of radish and lettuce seedlings,
and, at the back, last year's spinach plants. 6 Inter-planting cabbages,
lettuces, radishes, tomatoes and beans with pot and French marigolds, dwarf
convolvulus and sweet peas looks attractive and minimizes insect damage (see
p. 86). Changes in arrangement of the lawn bed are made from year to year,
hence the variation in the photographs.

generations of small white caterpillars pupate on the foodplant, and more of the variable pupae are green than brown. Later generations leave food-plants, often travelling some distance, to pupate and over-winter on more permanent structures, and more tend to be brown than green. Whatever your feelings with regard to the effect of cabbage whites on cabbages and other brassica crops, their first appearance is confirmation that winter is over. What more summery image is there of the garden, than one of flowers alive with butterflies?

It is so easy to be diverted into watching birds and the first butterflies, that the tasks of maintaining the garden are neglected. But it is still cool, too cool to sit still watching animal life for long. What better way of keeping warm than useful activity? As April begins, there is plenty to do in the garden, both gardening tasks and arranging various ways of monitoring insect activity.

PLATE 4   7 Runner beans and sweet peas form dense hedges round the lawn bed in August, and nicotiana dominates the mixed planting of vegetables and flowers. In the morning sun, it is alive with bees, butterflies, hoverflies and other insects. 8 Cabbages show few signs of insect damage when inter-planted with aromatic French marigolds. The bare patch is where radishes and lettuces have been harvested.

4

APRIL

Setting traps

The growing season has begun in earnest, and everywhere I look, crisp, tender greenery is pushing from the ground or from once-bare brown twigs. Clusters of downy leaves of perennial cornflower enclosing hard buds criss-crossed with black, and lush comfrey leaves spring up all over the place, from root fragments missed when I tried to curb their spread. Self-sown columbines (*Aquilegia*) sprout tiers of frilly leaflets, and there are far more hollyhocks, with their robust crinkly leaves, than I had planned. Ivy-leaved speedwell sprawls across bare patches of soil, although I was sure I had pulled out last year's plants before they could set seed. Fleshy lovage spikes unfurl large, pink-flushed leaves, tight fennel shoots break into soft, green filaments, and the shiny, purplish-brown, new stems of goat's beard (*Aruncus sylvester*) uncurl bronzed young leaves. Silver birch, raspberry canes, and the winter-brown tangle of mock orange (*Philadelphus*) are tinged with green, and tight, greyish leaf buds appear on the rowan. Early spring flowers pale beside deep blue, fragrant drifts of grape hyacinths, the first red tulips blaze like beacons, and long-stemmed pink flowers of bleeding heart (*Dicentra*) waft gently to and fro in the breeze.

Honeybees, the pollen baskets on their hind legs crammed full, are busy at the grape hyacinths, scrambling to retain a footing below each tiny, constricted bell, as they harvest its pollen and nectar. The first freshly-emerged hoverflies of the year are feeding at flowers and basking in the sun; most are slender, dark *Platycheirus* or *Melanostoma*, rather undistinguished-looking, but a larger *Metasyrphus*, black with pairs of yellow lunules on its abdomen, is feeding on one of the dazzlingly white flower clusters of perennial candytuft (*Iberis semper-virens*). A large, black and yellow queen wasp, newly emerged from hibernation, alights to lap water from the pond. The gooseberry patch is humming with bees, busily feeding at the insignificant green flowers. The visitors are various small black, yellowish or rufous solitary bees, some of them resembling honeybees, others quite furry. Less than a week after the flowers first opened, tiny gooseberries are beginning to develop as a result of pollen transfer during the bees' feeding visits. In parts of the garden, where soil is sandy, are small holes surrounded by conical heaps of fine, granular soil, like miniature volcanoes; these are newly excavated entrances to burrows of solitary mining bees (*Andrena*). Bumblebees hum around patches of spotted dead-nettle, some black with red tails, some tawny, others black and yellow with white, brownish or pinky-red tails.

Bumblebees are able to fly earlier in the year and in colder weather than most other insects, because they maintain an internal temperature of 30-37°C, even when their surroundings are near freezing point. An insect weighing less than a gram achieves this prodigious feat by operating its own central heating system. The physiology of the flight muscles, within the thorax, is such that heat is generated by chemical processes while a bumblebee is at rest. Consequently, it can warm up the flight muscles prior to flight, and retain heat in the thorax after alighting. So restricted and specialized is this heat production system, that only the flight muscles and thorax warm up, while the abdomen remains quite cool. Close-set hairs give insulation, and a rotund shape also helps, because surface area is small relative to volume, and hence the tendency to lose heat is small relative to the capacity to produce it.

Although I know my patch well, as I walk around I see few insects that I can identify with certainty. I can describe many different sorts in some detail, but almost every description would fit several species. There are, for instance, six similar species of black and yellow social wasps belonging to the family Vespidae in Britain. Some bumblebees can be identified as they feed at flowers, but it is impossible to distinguish between two of the white-tailed black and yellow species without closer examination, and there are confusingly many species of solitary bees. Numerous species of hoverflies are slender and dark, and many more have paired white or yellow spots or lunules on a black abdomen. Although I can watch insects in my garden with interest and pleasure, I can only gain a generalized idea of who is there. To discover anything further, I need to identify insects to species, and if I am to do that, I must first catch them.

Catching insects

One way of catching insects is by hand-netting, and I often carry a net when strolling round the garden, so that I can take a closer look at anything interesting. Butterflies can readily be identified to species, but this is not the case with most other sorts of insects, even when they are confined in a net or transferred to a glass jar. Many of the differences between closely related species are so small that use of a lens or even a microscope is necessary; fine detail can only be seen clearly on an immobilized insect, and for most practical purposes this means a dead one. There would be no pleasure in indiscriminate slaughter of insects that I am watching and enjoying as I work in the garden, so use of hand-netting as a means of identification and monitoring abundance is limited to butterflies.

From 1972 to 1979, I made a consistent effort to hand-net as many butterflies as possible in the garden. Obviously this could not be a continuous operation, but everyone in the family took part, and as people are happy to be outside on sunny days when butterflies too are active, a reasonable proportion of those visiting the garden was caught. The object of the exercise was to find out how many individuals and species occur in a garden. No one could see, let alone catch, every individual, but regular forays with a butterfly net provided a sample of total numbers present throughout the summer. As well as providing species lists for each year, this gave a means of comparing abundance and variety from month to month and year to year. Each individual caught was marked on one wing with a spot of waterproof ink from a felt-tipped pen, to ensure that it was recorded only once, and could then be released unharmed. You should not embark on such an investigation, however, unless expert tuition is available; handling live butterflies without damaging them in any way requires a delicate touch.

There are disadvantages to taking samples of insects in this way, since you can only catch those you see, and many that are chased elude capture. The total catch could thus be biassed towards conspicuous, slower-moving species. It is necessary to search systematically flowers where butterflies might be feeding, and to follow each sighting through to successful capture, however much strenuous sprinting and leaping is called for. It is one way of keeping fit, I suppose! Honesty is essential if the catch is to be an accurate sample in terms of its species composition. For every painted lady that visits the garden, there are hundreds of small cabbage whites, but abandoning pursuit of a cabbage white, and going to great lengths to capture the first painted lady of the year, would introduce bias. A sample should reflect the larger assemblage of which it is a part, just as an opinion poll should reflect the opinions of the population at large. If three species occur in the ratio 4:2:1, then, in a sample of 350, there should be approximately 200 of the first, 100 of the second, and 50 of the third; but if the ratio of the same species is 400:200:1, the third species may not occur at all in a sample of 350.

Hand-netting works as a means of sampling butterflies, because they are large, conspicuous, easily identified, and readily marked. Investigation of other groups of garden insects, and other sorts of invertebrate animals, necessitates using various designs of traps. It might seem odd that I should use traps in a garden whose animal life affords me so much interest and pleasure, but there is no way of finding out exactly who is in the garden, when they are there, and in what numbers, other than systematically collecting samples which can be identified to species. Collection of a sample removes only an unselected fraction of the animal community, involving nothing like the wholesale destruction wrought by gardeners using pesticides, yet trapping has led to the discovery of many rare and unusual insects. For instance, one species of ichneumonid trapped in my garden had only been recorded once before in Britain, and that was in 1911, at King's Lynn, Norfolk. There is a special need for establishing what insects and other animals occur in gardens, because ecologists and conservationists tend to dismiss them as barren habitats, and to assume that, being man-made, they are devoid of interest and irrelevant to preservation of our fauna. The only way of championing the cause of gardens as habitats full of interest, variety and value, is by presentation of firm evidence. Belief, however fervently expressed, is not enough. Instead, we need to know with certainty what species are there, how numbers fluctuate seasonally and annually, and how the species composition of the fauna changes from time to time.

The main requirement of a trapping method is that it supplies as unselected a sample as possible, but every sort of trap is more effective in capturing some groups of animals than others. A light trap, for instance, only captures insects that fly at night and are attracted to light; it is thus particularly effective for sampling moths (although can give no information about wingless females), but also captures small numbers of other sorts of nocturnal insects, as well as a few diurnal ones that happen to be within range of the light. Whatever method is used, trapping results can be adequately interpreted only if the limitations of the method are clearly understood. Siting of a trap is also important. Some insects frequent dense undergrowth, others like sunshine, but few fly in strong wind, and so a trap that captures flying insects is most effective in a relatively sheltered situation. Since both nocturnal and diurnal insects have daily and seasonal peaks of activity, the most satisfactory traps are those that operate continuously day and night, summer and winter, in all weathers. We have then two criteria for trapping: that it should be as unselective as possible, and that it should be continuous. Malaise and pitfall traps satisfy these criteria, and I use both in the garden.

However valid the reasons for trapping, a biologist is not absolved from responsibilities, and should observe a code of conduct. There can be no excuse or justification for wanton damage and destruction. Hence my word of warning about catching butterflies 'just for fun'. When my children were small, both they and their friends insisted on 'helping', it was a rule that netted butterflies should be brought straight to me, the only one who was allowed to handle and mark them. Care and thought are also necessary in the operation of traps. The model of light trap I use does not kill moths, but once captured they remain motionless, and next day most can be identified and released. There would be no point in doing this when the trap is surrounded by eager, hungry-looking sparrows (who quickly learn what is inside, and are not above joining the moths in the trap). The only realistic course is to keep the moths safely in the trap, with a butterfly net over the opening, until dusk, when sparrows have gone to roost but moths are active and can fly away. Similarly, it would be irresponsible to leave a trap full of moths to bake in the sun, so it is moved into deep shade to keep cool.

The traps

The first of April is a red-letter day in my garden calendar, the date on which I erect the Malaise trap and sink the pitfalls. I have tried leaving the Malaise trap up all winter, but it caught little between 31 October and 1 April, and winter storms inflicted considerable damage on its fabric. The trap is an open-sided, tent-like structure of meshed fabric, about two metres long and 1.3 metres wide. The pitched roof, also made of netting, rises obliquely to a peak about two metres high at one end, where there is an opening leading into a collecting jar, containing 70 per cent ethyl alcohol as killing agent and preservative. Tape loops, sewn to the top and bottom of each corner and the middle of the end walls, are tied onto poles firmly driven into the ground, the collecting jar is supported by an extra long pole, and all poles are anchored by guy ropes. An internal baffle of netting runs along the long axis of the trap, and also divides the roof space almost up to the opening into the collecting jar.

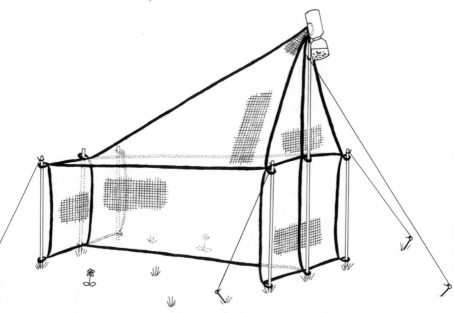

MALAISE TRAP

Black netting is used for baffle and end walls up to the height of the lower edge of the roof, and white netting for the upper parts and the sloping panels of the roof. The openings at the sides are each about 1.1 metres high and the length of the trap. Flying insects that enter the sides and strike the internal baffle, tend to clamber or fly upwards, and eventually fall into the collecting jar. This is encouraged by the colour of different panels, since black and white mesh are not obvious as barriers against vegetation and sky, respectively. The behaviour of insects on encountering the internal baffle is like that of insects trapped in the house, which fly to a window and then fly or walk to the top of the pane.

Over the years, I have made a number of Malaise traps on a small portable sewing machine, and developed considerable sympathy with tent- and sail-makers, as I got lost in the voluminous folds, always seeming to end up on the opposite side of the fabric from the needle (which had usually broken). Cutting out the panels from fine netting (similar to that used for net curtains) can only be done on a large, flat surface; I find the lawn is ideal for this, but just as I start to cut, the wind blows, and cut and uncut fabric billow teasingly around the scissors. It is now possible to buy ready-made traps, and I have gladly relinquished the task! If an old trap is to be used again, it first has to be spread out and checked carefully for holes, tears and missing ties, for sewing repairs are tricky once it is in position.

Erecting the trap is rather like putting up a tent, requiring two people if it is to be accomplished quickly and efficiently. Every year I use the same site, one that at the outset just 'looked likely'. The pole supporting the collecting jar is set in the gully surrounding the lawn, with the other end of the trap just in the raspberry patch; there are lilac and broom bushes backed by a fence to one side, and the other is open to the garden. Beneath is a mixture of spotted dead-nettle, grape hyacinths, feverfew, yarrow, creeping-Jenny (*Lysimachia nummularia*), Michaelmas daisies, reflexed stonecrop and other plants. An American entomologist and world authority on the Ichneumonidae, Henry Townes (who designed the model of Malaise trap that I use, and has operated them all over the world), took one look at the site I had chosen and predicted a poor catch. Since intuition tempered by experience is the best guide for positioning traps, I was tempted to move mine, but decided not to. My decision is vindicated by the large catch, particularly of ichneumonids, which compares favourably with those from Malaise traps operated in other sites, including tropical gardens. By chance, the trap is set in a flight path used by insects of many sorts. Butterflies, in particular, tend to come into the garden over the fence in the northwest corner, and then fly diagonally across rockery, vegetable patch and fruit bushes, towards the northeast corner of the lawn. This brings them up against one side of the trap. Those that miss it, fly down a herbaceous border along the east side of the back garden, rise to clear the shrubbery that flanks the east side of the house, and either fly away immediately, or visit the front garden and then leave, usually in a southeasterly or southerly direction.

A Malaise trap uses no attractant, simply intercepting insects in their normal flight. Some find their way out, but the trap collects a representative sample. Although a Malaise trap provides an adequate sample of ladybirds and small beetles, it rarely catches larger beetles, which tend to drop to the ground on meeting the baffle, and then walk away. Otherwise, it is a most satisfactory means of monitoring the flight activities of insects, and has provided more information about the garden fauna than any other sampling method. On a hot, still day, so many insects are caught that the contents of the collecting jar look like an unusual and unappetizing soup. An objection regularly raised by critical visitors is that such a collecting method must drastically deplete the garden fauna. The argument against this view is that the trap only catches those insects that wander into 2.9 cubic metres of air space, and only a proportion (for ichneumonids, about 20 per cent) of those. This can only be a tiny fraction of the insects present in the garden. Moreover, I know from trapping and hand-netting, that garden insects are continually on the move, circulating through the whole complex of surrounding suburbia, so that any removed from my garden are soon replaced. Far from having any worries about using a Malaise trap as a sampling method, had I not done so, I should never have discovered how abundant and rich the insect fauna is.

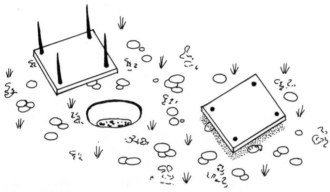

PITFALL TRAPS

Pitfall traps catch small animals walking over the soil surface, such as ground beetles, centipedes, spiders and their allies, and some of the larger flightless insects. As with the Malaise trap, there is no point in operating pitfalls when invertebrates are inactivated by low temperatures, so these too are used from April to October inclusive. Having erected the Malaise trap, the next job is to sink the pitfalls. Doing this from scratch is a tedious job, because the container that forms the trap must be sunk with its rim flush with the soil surface; if it projects, making a 'step', little is caught, but if sunk too far, soil washes or falls in. The secret is to choose permanent sites, and sink short lengths of plastic piping into the ground. Replaceable plastic cups can then be dropped into the tops of the pipes to serve as the actual traps. The cups are half-filled with a weak solution of formaldehyde, which quickly kills and preserves any invertebrates that fall in. To cut down collection of leaf litter and other debris, each trap is covered with a square of board supported by nails hammered down through the corners. The board is pushed down until there is about two centimetres clearance above the soil surface, sufficient to admit wandering invertebrates, but not mice or other small mammals. I operate eleven pitfalls in all, two in the rockery, four in herbaceous borders, two in the shrubbery, and three below the Malaise trap.

The catch

At the end of the first week in April comes the welcome and exciting task of sorting through the first Malaise trap sample of the year. What will it contain? Will the insects signal an early start to the season? Will there be something new or unusual? Despite high hopes, the first weekly trap sample is small; there may be a 2-spot ladybird, and a 7-spot, a few small, dark hoverflies, a couple of bumblebees, a small moth, a number of solitary bees, a queen wasp, and an assortment of tiny bugs and flies. As the month progresses, the catch improves, although it depends very much on the weather and how advanced the season is.

The trap jar is emptied every week, as a routine Sunday job. The contents are poured into a white enamel tray and sorted into different groups. In warm weather, this is best done outside, on the garden table, to take advantage of the bright light; usually it has to be done indoors, and a powerful lamp is needed. The catch is carefully and minutely examined, specimen by specimen, and selected groups are removed with fine forceps to appropriately labelled jars of clean alcohol. It would be a truly daunting task to sort out, let alone identify, all the insects caught, so I concentrate on particular groups that I, or someone known to me, have the necessary experience and time to deal with. Hoverflies, ladybirds and Lepidoptera (moths and butterflies) are extracted as weekly samples, bees and wasps monthly, and ants, lacewings and their allies (Neuroptera), sawflies, earwigs, beetles other than ladybirds, and bugs (Hemiptera), excluding aphids, annually. The remainder is set aside, on a monthly basis, until such time as it becomes practicable to extract another group. When I started trapping, for instance, I ignored Neuroptera, but, having found someone willing to identify them, am now going back to previous years' 'remainders', and taking them out. Pitfalls are emptied and formalin replaced every week or two, so that debris can be removed and the effective operation of the traps guaranteed.

A Malaise trap is a highly efficient means of collecting a large sample of insects, but the catch is of no value unless at least some of the groups it contains can be identified to species. This is no easy task, even with the larger, more familiar insects, and with tiny, diverse insects, such as parasitic wasps, is a painstaking, time-consuming job for an expert. My husband, Denis, has acquired, over a lifetime, the knowledge and experience to deal with Lepidoptera and, since I started operating the trap, has learnt how to identify ladybirds. By using published keys, referring to museum collections, and consulting experts over problems, I have taught myself how to identify hoverflies and bumblebees. For the rest, I am largely dependent on goodwill and cooperation, which enable me to tap the enormous fund of knowledge and community of interest that exists among biologists. For instance, in 1972-74, I sorted all Ichneumonidae from trap samples and sent them to Henry Townes. Thanks to him, we have garden records of 530 species of Ichneumonidae; not only is this more than a quarter of the total ichneumonid fauna of the British Isles, but it includes new British records and species new to science.

I am aware of hoverflies and bumblebees in the garden in April, but Malaise trap samples can tell me more about them. Over the period 1972-81, the trap has caught more than 30,000 hoverflies of 91 species, but most are caught in mid-summer. The best April catch was in 1972, when 18 individuals of five species were caught; the worst year was 1977 when none was caught. In ten years, 12 species entered the trap in April. Most occur throughout the summer, but small, dark *Platycheirus ambiguus*, indistinguishable in the garden from other species of *Platycheirus*, are only caught early in the year, rarely occurring later than May. Occasionally, the more familiar, medium-sized hoverflies, with yellow bands or paired yellow spots on the black abdomen, are trapped in April, but most of those caught are small and inconspicuous. There are eight species of bumblebees (*Bombus*) in my garden, and all have occurred in April Malaise trap samples; the best years were 1975 and 1976, when April catches included seven species (not the same seven each year). *Bombus terrestris*, yellow- and black-banded, with a cream-coloured or tawny tail, and *B. agrorum*, rufous-brown without bands, occur in April every year, and *B. pratorum*, yellow- and black-banded with a pinky-orange tail, in most years. Of the four species of cuckoo bumblebees (*Psithyrus*) recorded from the garden, only one has been caught in April.

Social life

The appearance of queen wasps and bumblebees from hibernation is a good point at which to consider social life in wasps and bees and its implications. Most wasps and bees are not easy to identify to species, and this is another group for which I enlisted the help of a specialist. I now know that there is a total of 86 species of bees and wasps (apart from the tiny parasitic wasps that lack a sting) in the garden, but have seen few of them alive in the sense of knowing what I was looking at. Most are solitary, a number are social, some are parasitic, and others are social parasites. The first thing is to distinguish between bees and wasps. Bees feed as adults and larvae on pollen and nectar, most are more or less covered with branched hairs which are often modified into pollen-collecting structures, and most have rather long tongues for lapping nectar. Wasps eat nectar and other sugary fluids, but feed their larvae on animal food; they are smooth, not hairy, and their tongues are short. A child's 'wops' or 'wapsy' is a pleasing reminder of the Anglo-Saxon *waeps*, before pronunciation changed to 'wasp'.

Because wasp and bee larvae are helpless, dependent upon food supplied by their mother or another adult, the number of young that individuals of a solitary species can raise is limited. Social species, however, first produce one or more batches of workers, which cooperate in raising the rest of their mother's brood, so that she can make a greater contribution to the next generation. It is not the same as cooperation in human society, because worker bees and wasps, like worker ants, are non-functional females, usually sterile, but at any rate unable to produce eggs except in the unlikely event of the egg-laying queen's premature death. Moreover, they never mate, and consequently can only lay unfertilized eggs. Sex determination in Hymenoptera (ants, bees and wasps) depends on egg fertilization, fertilized eggs developing into females, unfertilized into males. A mated queen can lay both sorts, because she can control liberation of sperm from the organ in which they are stored during copulation. Since worker females rarely lay eggs, and then produce only males, their contribution to the next generation is minimal. The lives of males have been pared down to their sexual function; they take no part in colony life, and in most species of bees and wasps are only produced in the autumn, at the end of the lifespan of a colony, so that fertile females, produced at the same time, are able to mate prior to hibernation.

The workers of a colony are all offspring of its queen, who only mates once, and therefore are genetically similar, not only to each other, but also to the new queens and males (their sisters and brothers) that their mother produces later in the colony's life. Their adaptation as workers, rather than reproductives, safe-guards the queen's contribution to the next generation. There is nothing altruistic in the workers' behaviour, because they carry the same genes as reproductives. They are working to ensure perpetuation by their reproductive brothers and sisters of the genes that they share with them. This means, however, that from an evolutionary point of view workers are not individuals, for the colony's contribution to the next generation, in the form of new queens and males, is through the queen alone.

Wasps – the hunters

Most species of garden wasps are solitary. There are 26 species of digger wasps (Sphecidae) in my garden, many of which excavate nests in the ground, although some use hollow stems. Each female constructs a small group of individual cells, stocks each with enough live prey (paralysed by stinging) to sustain the developing larva, and lays an egg on the last prey item brought in. They never return to the nests after egg-laying, and have no contact with their offspring. *Trypoxylon* are rather elongate black wasps that provision their nests with spiders, and black and yellow *Ectemnius* use flies, including hoverflies that females catch while they are both feeding at flowers. The commonest garden species, however, belong to the genus *Pemphredon*, which excavate nests in stems, softened by the feeding activities of beetle grubs, and stock separate thin-walled cells with aphids. *P.lugubris*, an abundant species, is black and rather stouter than *Trypoxylon*. I also have two species of mason wasps. These are also solitary, but belong to the family Vespidae, easily distinguished from sphecid wasps by the wings, which are folded lengthways along the sides of the body when at rest, rather than lying flat over the back. Each female excavates three or four cells in sandy soil or crumbling masonry, lays an egg in each, and then stocks it with paralysed caterpillars. Like most digger wasps, mason wasps practice mass provisioning of cells and have no contact with their developing larvae, but there is one important difference, in that the egg is laid before the cell is stocked. Thus there is a tenuous link between mother and offspring, since she has to return to her eggs to stock the cells with food. Other wasps, such as the active, brightly-coloured ruby-tailed wasp (*Chrysis ignita*), are parasitic on solitary bees or wasps; they lay their eggs individually in occupied cells, and their larvae feed on the occupants, sometimes eating the stored food as well. I have six species of this type of parasitic wasp in the garden, the commonest of which uses *Pemphredon lugubris* as its host.

The overwhelming majority of wasps in a garden, such as those that harass the picnic table, belong to two species of yellow and black social wasps, *Vespula vulgaris* and *V.germanica*. The life history of social wasps is quite different from that of digger and mason wasps; each queen produces sterile workers, often in several batches over a considerable period of time, before she lays eggs that give males and functional females. The workers take over maintenance and expansion of the nest, and care of the developing brood, so that the queen becomes little more than an egg-producing machine. Nests become large and populous, although they only last for one season and the structure, even if it persists, is never reoccupied. The history of a colony begins when fertile females, destined to be next year's queens, emerge in mid-summer to autumn (depending on species), and mate prior to hibernating. Over-wintered queens emerge in early spring to early summer, again depend-ing on species, and soon start building nests. I have five species of social wasps in the garden, three *Vespula* and two *Dolichovespula*, and have once recorded the cuckoo wasp, *V.austriaca*, females of which usurp *V.rufa* queens and appropriate their nests and workers; all have the character-istic black and yellow wasp pattern. In general, *Vespula* species nest underground, or in enclosed cavities, such as holes in roofs, while *Dolichovespula* build aerial nests in exposed or semi-exposed positions on trees. One year, a large *Vespula* colony was established beneath a mat of saxifrage sprawling from the rockery over an adjacent path. The entrance was on the path side, deterring me somewhat from my customary habit of walking the garden barefoot in summer.

The nest fabric is made of wood fibres mixed with saliva into a paste, which soon dries into a papery material. The wood fibres are rasped from any accessible wooden surface, such as fence posts or raspberry canes, using the strong jaws, and the shallow, gouged marks left after wood has been collected can often be recognized on untreated fences and garden furniture. *V.germanica* collects sound wood, *V.vulgaris* uses slightly rotten wood, and the resulting greyish 'paper' differs in texture, colour and strength, that of *V.vulgaris* being yellower and more brittle. The queen constructs a small cluster of cells, suspended by a central stalk from a hanging triangular sheet of 'paper', and lays an egg in each. At the same time she makes a start on the first layer of the nest envelope, by building outwards from the stalk or suspension sheet. She goes on adding new cells round the edge of the original cluster, and as each cell becomes surrounded by others it assumes a hexagonal shape. When the eggs hatch, the queen forages for caterpillars and other soft-bodied insects, and for morsels cut from dead animals, which she chews into pellets and feeds to the larvae – a bit like a diet of insect hamburger. Fully grown larvae spin silken lids for their cells before pupating. When the first batch of new adults bite their way out of their enclosed cells, the character of the nest changes, for these are worker females that take over all duties of building, foraging for food, bringing drops of water and fanning the nest to cool it, and defending it against intruders. Thereafter, the queen's only job is to lay eggs.

With the queen's energies devoted to egg production, and a workforce of sterile females to care for the young, the nest grows rapidly. New combs of cells are suspended in tiers below the original one, and the whole is enclosed in several overlapping, dome-shaped envelopes of 'paper', which both protect and insulate the brood combs. Nests of *V.vulgaris* may finally consist of as many as 12 combs composed of more than 15,000 cells, although this is exceptional, and nests of some of the other species are considerably smaller. The life of individual *V.vulgaris* workers is short, often only a matter of days, but during the course of a season, a nest of about 10,000 cells produces more than 10,000 workers and about a thousand each of males and females. When males and fertile females have been produced, no more young are raised and the colony gradually disintegrates. Workers and males die, and only fertilized females – next year's queens – go into hibernation. *Dolichovespula* species and *Vespula rufa* have relatively short seasons, producing new queens a month or two before *V.vulgaris* and *V.germanica*. Hibernated queens of the cuckoo wasp, *V.austriaca*, do not emerge until *V.rufa* nests are well-established, and then produce only males and new queens.

Bees – the gatherers
Honeybees (which are not native to Britain) and bumblebees are social, but there are many more species of solitary bees, including a number of different sorts of cuckoo bees, whose young, like cuckoos, feed at the expense of their host's offspring. We have already met some of the solitary bees that fly early in the year, such as flower or potter bees (*Anthophora*) and mining bees (*Andrena*). Large numbers of furry, rufous-coloured lawn bees (*Andrena armata*), which busy themselves around gooseberry flowers, often burrow into lawns, where they throw up little conical heaps of fine, sandy soil. *Osmia rufa*, which nests in holes in walls and tree stumps, is a hairy, tawny-coloured bee, which, when viewed under the microscope, always looks to me as though it is wearing one of those once-fashionable fur coats made of alternate bands of shaggy fur and a smooth satiny material. There are many other solitary bees in the garden, such as *Colletes daviesana*, which nests in burrows in soil or masonry and fills its papery cells with honey, and leaf-cutting bees (*Megachile*), which cut smooth-edged semicircular pieces from the

leaves of roses and other plants, and use them, neatly rolled, to make cells in hollow plant stems or other secluded places. Occasionally, the Malaise trap catches species of *Halictus*, mining bees that show rudimentary social behaviour; females hibernate after mating, and although they mass-provision their burrows with pollen and honey, they stand guard over their nests so that they have some contact with their offspring. One southern British species of *Halictus* rears a single batch of workers which cooperate in raising males and queens. On a few occasions, I have caught species of *Nomada* and *Sphecodes*, which are parasitic on *Andrena* and *Halictus*, eating stored pollen and honey, and occasionally the host larvae as well. Some are brightly coloured like wasps, and they are much less hairy than their relatives, since they never collect pollen.

Social bees differ in several respects from social wasps. They construct brood cells from wax, which is secreted by special cells in the abdomen. Wax is extruded between the abdominal segments as thin sheets, removed with the hind legs, and moulded with the jaws. Bee larvae receive a vegetarian diet of pollen and honey. The exact composition of bumblebee honey is not known, but is probably similar to that made by honeybees. Collected nectar is transported in an enlarged section of the digestive tract, where enzymes convert complex sugars to simpler ones, and then regurgitated into storage cells as honey, which becomes concentrated by evaporation. A bumblebee can collect so much flower nectar that her distensible honey stomach swells up like a tiny balloon until it accommodates a weight almost equal to her own.

Bumblebee colonies, like those of social wasps, last for only one season, although the actual duration varies greatly from one species to another. Mated females, next year's queens, hibernate in a secluded nook or cranny – a sleepy, white-tailed *Bombus lucorum* queen crawled from a log drying on my hearth, one cold winter day – emerging in spring to search for a nesting site. Some species nest above ground beneath heaps of dead grass or other vegetation, others nest underground in abandoned mouse nests. The queen hollows out a chamber amid the dead grass or old mouse nesting material, and constructs a waxen cell around a mass of pollen on which she lays several eggs. At the same time, she makes a wax honey-pot, near the nest entrance, in which she keeps honey to tide herself over periods of bad weather when foraging is difficult. Once the larvae hatch and begin to feed, she supplies them with honey and more pollen, and incubates them with the heat generated by her furry body. Each fully grown larva spins an individual silken cocoon for pupation, and the queen then removes their waxen brood chamber. She recycles the wax, using it to build new brood cells on the outer, upper edge of the cluster of cocoons. Bumblebee combs grow piece-meal, expanding upwards and outwards in an irregular fashion, with a hollow in the middle caused by the pressure of the body of the incubating queen. Once the first batch of workers have emerged, the empty cocoons are used for storing pollen and honey.

Newly emerged workers are weak and bedraggled, but in a day or two the wings harden, the coat dries and fluffs up, and they are ready to start work. Once workers are fit to forage, queen bumblebees stay at home, occupying themselves with cell construction, egg-laying, feeding the larvae, and incubation. The colony begins to grow, and those of some species become quite large: a nest of *B.terrestris* may have a comb 20-25 centimetres in diameter, and produce 300-400 workers. As a colony increases in size, the ratio of workers to larvae, and hence the food ration of each larva, increases; it seems to be this that leads to development of new queens, and males are produced at the same time. Males leave the nest and hang around entrances to other colonies of the same species, awaiting virgin females; this avoids the inbreeding that would result from mating with their sisters. The young queens, unlike those in wasp nests, take part in many household duties, but after males and females have emerged, no more workers are produced, and the colony gradually disintegrates. By this time, the founding queen is battered and tattered, and she, the workers and the males eventually die, only young, impregnated queens surviving the winter.

The life history of cuckoo bumblebees (*Psithyrus*) is quite different, for they are social parasites. Egg-laying females infiltrate nests of bumblebees, often, though not always, kill the queen, and depend on bumblebee workers to feed and tend their young. The outer skin, or cuticle, of cuckoo bees is shiny and hard, and shows through the covering of hair. Since they never collect food for a developing brood, they have no pollen baskets. Each species looks somewhat like the species of bumblebee that it parasitizes, but the deception that facilitates entry to a nest is that they share their host's odour. In general, over-wintered females emerge from hibernation later than bumblebees, not appearing until bumblebee nests contain workers that they can exploit.

Honeybees, which also forage for food in my garden, have a highly organized social life. Colonies are large, perennial, and bud off new colonies by swarming. The workers are sterile, and their age determines the tasks they perform. Chemical messenger substances, produced by the queen and circulated through the colony by mouth to mouth food exchange, inhibit development of workers' ovaries, prevent queen production, and generally hold the colony together. A bumblebee colony is better able to respond to change, because it has less cohesion. Larger workers usually forage and smaller ones perform tasks in the nest, but there is no rigidity about this, and if either work force is depleted, some of the others change jobs. At least some workers are capable of egg-laying, and do so if the queen dies, and also towards the end of the colony's life. The development of workers' ovaries is governed partly by abundance of food – more is available in a queen-less or old colony – and partly by social interactions. The queen, who actively defends her eggs and brood cells, heads a dominance hierarchy of workers, but if she is lost, the top worker assumes both her social position and her reproductive function, although all her offspring are male.

Next time you watch a ponderous bumblebee zooming from flower to flower with laden pollen baskets, on a lazy summer afternoon, remember how hard she works for her mother. Her apparently altruistic behaviour safe-guards the genes they share, and is innate and unreasoned. Her motivation is no more than instinct, from the Latin *stingere* (to goad), and each furry little worker is indeed goaded by a force that we can explain, but find hard to comprehend.

Summer beckons

Yellow *Mahonia* petals have fallen, and through each skeletal spray pushes a tight sheath of pallid, overlapping bracts enclosing glossy, red-tinted foliage. Sombre hollies are decorated with tiny clusters of bright, new leaves, their prickles also tinged with red. Shoots sprouting from a persistent sycamore stump bear leaves the colour of tarnished copper; the first, rounded mint leaves clasp the stout stems so tightly that only their purplish undersides show; and the bouffant, icing-sugar pink blossoms of Japanese cherry are interspersed with new foliage so red that from a distance the tree seems to have two sorts of flowers. The new growth of many plants is red or purple, looking quite unlike tender, green leaves. Is this perhaps deception, practised as a deterrent to herbivorous insects? The first pansy lifts its face to the sun, the gold flowers of Leopard's bane nod in the breeze, and sprays of tight buds peep from the leafy cowls of lilies-of-the-valley. Pink-flowering saxifrage is already in bloom, well ahead of the white variety; saxifrage, derived from the Latin *frangere* (to break) and *saxum* (rock), is an ironic name for such a delicate plant.

An article in *The Times* tells me 'We are now moving into pest and disease time . . . so we should take a walk round the garden every two or three days looking for trouble.' That does not sound much fun. To be fair to the writer, he understands the effects of poisons on wildlife, but his interest is in producing the finest plants and the best garden displays, and concern for other garden inhabitants is by choice subordinated to this interest. I appreciate this viewpoint, but do not happen to share it. Another gardening column headed 'Jobs for April' induces a mild state of panic; if I paid too much attention to the list, I should be working non-stop, day in, day out. Earnest gardeners rarely approve of the rather muddled way I do things, but it always seems to work out in the end. Even though I ignore many of the conventions, it is clear, I hope, that I do a lot of work in the garden, and I am glad that I have already sown seeds that have to be grown in boxes indoors. In some years, I have started tomatoes, sweet peas, African and French marigolds (*Tagetes*), and others in March, but this always seems to coincide with a late spring, and they have become unmanageably 'leggy' long before I dare move them outside. The broad, tile-covered window-sill behind the kitchen sink, and a disproportionate area of adjacent work-top, are requisitioned as temporary growing space, and seed boxes sometimes overflow into a sunny bedroom. The garden does seem to be invading the house, but what a thrill it is to watch seeds grow, and the proliferation of green seedlings on the kitchen window-sill is a great comfort to the tedium of dish-washing.

Vegetable beds can now be hoed over to discourage early weeds, and the soil prepared for lettuce, radish, cabbage and spring onion seeds. My feelings on the first day that I can really handle and work the soil must be rather like those of a sculptor when he first holds in his hands the clay from which he will eventually coax a work of art. What a pleasure it is to crumble warm soil into fine, moist granules. I fail to understand how anyone can garden in gloves; broken nails and cracked fingers ingrained with soil are a small price to pay for feeling the garden grow beneath my fingertips. In some parts of the country, barley farmers reputedly took off their trousers and sat on the ground to test its temperature and judge whether the soil was warm enough for sowing. I have never had the courage to try this – I do not think suburbia is quite the place for such a basic approach – but its common sense appeals to me.

The growing season gathers momentum, but the weather is untrustworthy. In late April 1981, strong winds, sleet and drifting snow laid the garden low overnight. A cold, white blanket weighed birch saplings down till their tips touched the ground, and made cypress, flowering cherry, privet and forsythia sprawl in ungainly fashion. In mid-winter, there are few leaves or flowers to catch and hold snow, but in April it settles and clings on to sappy, new growth too weak to take its weight. The thaw was rapid, but left the garden strewn with snapped tulips, scattered cherry blossom and torn leaves, and looking like a battlefield. The day before the storm, to my surprise, a wood mouse ran across the yard on two separate occasions; I had never seen one alive in the garden before, although I had found a corpse on the path a couple of years previously. The Chinese claim that unusual animal behaviour presages earthquakes and freak weather conditions, so perhaps that wood mouse was trying to tell me something. Not that anyone should need telling that spring weather is unpredictable. March to May 1979 was the wettest since 1727 and snow fell widely in the first week of May. April and May 1980 were the driest since 1896, followed by the wettest June since 1879.

Despite cold spring weather, newly-fledged blackbirds and thrushes, all wide yellow mouth, are hopping clumsily about, looking top-heavy until their tail feathers grow. A collared dove is calling with an unfamiliar intonation. There are two perched on the television aerial, and one is apparently addressing the other which is sitting tight and still beside him. He seems to be saying 'I love you . . . I love you . . .', with the accent on the second and highest note. On the 'I love . . .' he tips his head and body forwards towards his mate, straightening as he coos 'you'. Although the holes they once used are blocked, house sparrows with beaks full of straw, hop along the guttering of a neighbouring outhouse, trying to gain access to the roof space that, over the years, they had stuffed with nesting material. A merry splashing from above indicates that a hen blackbird is taking her daily bath in rain-water puddles in the blocked guttering on my own roof; she bathes with gusto, sending a cascade of water down to the ground, and it was some time before I realized why it seemed to rain from a clear sky. Alerted by her splashing, I glance out of the study window, and surprise a pair of courting hedge sparrows, circling round each other in little darting hops, with wings slightly depressed and quivering.

The birds have had a busy month, and so have I, what with setting traps, preparing soil and sowing seeds. Their nesting and my gardening activities have been interrupted and set back by unseasonal cold and snow, but May should bring more predictable weather. As the days lengthen, birds will be less hard-pressed to collect enough food for their young, and I shall be able to spend more time working in the garden and watching the rapidly increasing variety of insects.

5

MAY

Cuckoo-spit

At last I really feel I am getting somewhere. Seedlings started indoors have been hardened off: tomatoes and African marigolds already threaten to push the top off the cold frame, and the sweet peas have developed into a fine tangle of shoots and tendrils, enmeshing the other plants. Come rain or shine, they must be planted out. The first job is to put up stakes for the runner beans and sweet peas that will eventually form 'hedges' at the back and sides of a rectangular bed facing on to the lawn: paths run beside the lawn bed, so this arrangement of trellises makes for easy picking. This year I remember to buy plastic string to tie cross-struts and construct a 'ladder' for the sweet peas to climb; gardening twine may look better, but it takes house sparrows only a few days to unravel so many strands for nesting material that the structure becomes very rickety. Sparrows and blackbirds soon adopt the cross-struts as handy perches from which they engage in noisy slanging matches and keep an eye on feeding opportunities in the bed below – they also liberally spatter the spinach, close alongside the bean poles, with bird droppings.

The beans are now safely in the ground, although it always seems such a long wait before the arched stems push through the soil and drag the first pair of leaves safely up into the air. It is perhaps as well that I sowed generously, remembering the old adage: one for the rook, one for the crow, one to die, and one to grow. As I get down to the delicate task of transferring seedlings from pots or boxes to the ground, I get a different view of garden life. Centipedes tumble headlong from the sides of holes scooped out for tomato plants, and I inadvertently slice more than one earthworm. Woodlice and tiny wingless insects float briefly on the 'puddle' with which I irrigate each root cluster, then, as the water soaks in, scramble away, finally disappearing from view as I fill each hole with crumbled soil. I rarely see any slugs when planting out seedlings, but, sure enough, next day when I inspect my handiwork, I find most of the African marigolds (*Tagetes erecta*) mangled and collapsed. These seem to be the main target, although slugs often move on to aromatic French marigolds (*T.patula*), which I would expect to be unpalatable. Tomatoes are rarely touched, presumably because they are hairy as well as pungent, and the succulent sweet peas probably escape because I have already looped them up their 'ladder'.

Since I tolerate most plants, there are by definition few weeds in my garden; conventional gardeners' weeds are useful as soil cover, to retain moisture, and as shelter for predatory beetles and spiders, although some have to be removed, as there seems little point in shading out lettuces and cabbages, and converting all the soil nutrients into sow-thistles and groundsel. The many names used for groundsel over the centuries include 'grundy swallow', but it is possible that this refers not to its prodigious abilities to colonize new ground, but to its use by herbalists to make poultices; it has been suggested that 'grundy' or 'ground' are derived from *gund*, meaning pus. The paths are sprouting greenery along the cracks between the paving slabs, attractive at first, but soon becoming rather untidy, and needing attention. Creeping butter-cup and wood avens call for meticulous weeding lest they carpet the entire garden, and I have given up hope of controlling oxalis, but some of the 'weeds' are welcome, for seeds germinating in the compost spread on vegetable and flower beds include borage and pot marigolds (*Calendula officinalis*), and I shall leave many of these to provide colour and attract insects.

The welcome return of old friends
My attention is repeatedly distracted from planting and weeding as our local swifts, newly returned from Africa, wheel and scream overhead. Their arrival is so welcome that for the first few days after they arrive, I tend to stop whatever I am doing and watch their aerobatics every time I hear their excited calls, until my neck aches from looking skywards. House martins are back too. Despite their graceful flickering flight, they look almost dumpy beside the swifts; they seem to fly with more restraint, and certainly make less noise, although they hawk for aerial insects just as efficiently. The Malaise trap gives an indication of what is available to aerial hunters, for it contains an abundance of small flies and tiny green plant bugs, many small to medium-sized hoverflies, and a considerable number of winged aphids. The trap is catching low-flying

insects, but many get caught in updraughts and so become food for swifts and house martins.

Nectar-feeding is also getting under way as more flowers become available for insects to exploit. Hoverflies and other sorts of insects with short tongues, or proboscies, are restricted to flat, open flowers with readily accessible nectar, but they have a wide choice: creamy umbels of elder and rowan, snow-white clusters of spiraea, fragrant hawthorn and Mexican orange blossom (*Choisya ternata*), golden buttercups and creeping-Jenny, magenta crane's-bill (*Geranium cinereum*), and many others. Although some have quite long tongues, solitary bees visit many of the flowers that hoverflies can use, such as feathery pink tamarisk sprays, inconspicuous raspberry flowers, and the inviting yellow-centred white cups of strawberries, both wild and cultivated. Small bees are probably the main pollinators of raspberries and strawberries, and the gooseberry plants that they visited for food last month, are already hung with small, hairy berries. Long-tongued bumblebees are busy at more intricately-structured flowers, delving deep beneath the purplish-pink hoods of spotted dead-nettle, forcing open the keeled petals of broom, and clinging beneath the hanging bells of comfrey and spurred pink or purple flowers of columbine, as they reach for hidden nectar.

Red valerian in the herbaceous border and bright pink *Phlox douglasii* in the rockery are butterfly flowers, the petal bases forming a narrow tube that can only be probed by a butterfly's long, thin proboscis. Not that butterflies are restricted to tubular flowers. A solitary male orange-tip, tangerine-coloured blotches contrasting vividly with the white of the rest of its wings, visits the *Aubretia* to feed. The female lacks the orange patches, and might be mistaken for one of the cabbage white butterflies, although the greenish mottling of the undersides of the hind wings makes her far less conspicuous at rest. The caterpillars of orange-tip butterflies feed on the green seed-pods of a variety of wild cruciferous plants, such as hedge mustard. Not so long ago, they seemed to be becoming scarce, probably because of extensive use of herbicides on road verges. However, I have watched a female laying on *Arabis caucasica* (=*albida*) in my garden, and there are an increasing number of records of them using *Arabis* as a larval foodplant, suggesting that this attractive butterfly will establish itself as a garden resident.

May is not a good month for garden butterflies. Apart from orange-tips, a few over-wintered peacocks and small tortoiseshells, and the occasional brimstone, the only visitors are the ubiquitous white butterflies, mainly large and small cabbage whites, but also green-veined whites. The latter do not feed on cabbages, and are easily recognizable by the dusting of greenish-black scales along the veins on the underside of the wings. The three species of white butterflies, the orange-tip and the brimstone belong to the family Pieridae, a name, like so many scientific names, rooted in classical legend; the Pierides were the Muses, although this is small comfort to the gardener musing on the flutterings of cabbage whites around his vegetable patch.

Goldfinches are busily pecking at the flowers of perennial cornflower, although no seeds have formed as yet. Close inspection shows that the blue flowers are covered with tiny, green aphids, and it must be these that the finches are eating. Goldfinches are primarily weed seed-eaters; at the end of the nineteenth century, when farm labour was cheap and rough land was regularly scythed, they became quite rare. Since then, however, numbers have increased, especially in the last twenty years, and charms of goldfinches are once more a familiar sight.

Aphid numbers are building up all over the garden, on columbines, roses, elder and many other plants. The path beneath the apple tree is sticky with honeydew excreted by aphids feeding on tender, new leaves, and falling petals catch and smudge on the sugary patches. Ants run to and fro over clusters of aphids on the Lombardy poplar, palpating them with their antennae and licking up honeydew. Many of the leaf stalks of the poplar are curiously thickened and twisted into a tight spiral, a consequence of the activities of a gall-making aphid. I am puzzled to see ants on the globular green peony buds, which are just splitting to show the crimson petals within. The buds are slightly sticky, and the ants seem to be feeding, so, having brushed away an ant, I lick one of the buds and it proves to be quite sweet. A number of different sorts of plants have extra-floral nectaries, cherry laurel and some vetches at the base of the leaves, and trumpet creeper on the flower buds; their function seems to be to attract ants whose presence deters herbivorous insects. Floral nectaries of the double peonies, that are usually cultivated, are hidden deep within the flamboyant cluster of petals, and none of the winged nectar-feeders can reach them. I am glad to see that ants, at least, can use the peonies for food!

As I walk around the garden there is so much to see and enjoy. It seems to grow and change in character almost daily. Dense shade is developing under the horse chestnut and birch trees, and I can see that some judicious pruning will be called for if they are not to shade out many treasured plants. Indeed, the chestnut may have to go altogether as it prevents the sun from reaching the loganberries. Liverworts are spreading green, pancake-like growth over damp places in the yard. Ferns are sprouting in the rockery: their tightly rolled shoots, clothed in brown scales, uncoil day by day, reminding me first of boat prows, and then, as the lower leaflets expand, of fiddles, until finally the tall fronds are completely unfurled. The parsley, planted last year, has supplied enough to garnish my cooking all winter, but is now growing in earnest, in crisp curls. New shoots on the Norway spruce are like little rigid shaving-brushes of palest green, contrasting markedly with the sombre green of the old growth. Spiky sheaves of teasel leaves seem to increase in height daily, the hop plant that appeared last year is spiralling upwards at a rate that rivals Jack's beanstalk, and the umbrella-like leaves of rhubarb are shading succulent pink stalks. Lilacs scent the air by day, and lilies-of-the-valley perfume the evening. Indigo petals push through sheathing green bracts on tall iris stems, quickly unfurling like regal flags. The grape hyacinths are sadly over, their old flowering stems gaunt as miniature telegraph poles, but a welcome discovery is a common dog violet, flowering and growing vigorously amongst the broccoli.

A watery diet

About this time of year, little blobs of wet foam appear on many different sorts of garden plants. Equally familiar to farmers and countrymen, it is usually called cuckoo-spit, perhaps because its appearance coincides with the arrival of cuckoos, perhaps because they are held responsible. It has been attributed to a variety of other agents, hence the names frog spit, toad spit, snake's spit and witches' spit. One early botanist tried to classify plants according to their apparent abilities to produce foam, and the Swiss call the cuckoo flower (*Cardamine pratense*), the meadow foam plant. The sixteenth-century naturalist, Thomas Moufet (whose daughter, Patience, may well have been the Miss Muffet who was frightened from her tuffet by a spider), wrote: 'Also, from a whitish worm in frothy dew that in May sticks to plants a certain winged green creature is bred, in form like to the smallest kind of caterpillar, first it leaps, and afterwards it flies and therefore I fit to call it Locustella, a little locust. The English call the frothy matter Woodsear, as if you would say the putrefaction of wood. The Germans call it cuckow spittle.' Dr Moufet cannot have looked very closely at the occupant of cuckoo-spit. If you gently push aside the froth, you will find a tiny, green, wingless insect with its piercing mouthparts inserted in the plant; this is a larval stage, or nymph, of a spittlebug. The immature stages of several species of the family Cercopidae produce foam, but by far the commonest is the meadow spittlebug (*Philaenus spumarius*). The winged adults are rather frog-like and jump when disturbed; they are variable in colour, often brown, sometimes black or black and white. Eggs are laid in batches in late summer and autumn, usually on senescent plant material close to the ground, and do not hatch until the following spring. Young nymphs, like miniature adults but without wings, crawl to tender green plants, pierce the tissues with their mouth-stylets and start feeding.

But why the foam, and what is it? Spittlebugs tap a most unlikely source of food, the xylem vessels of plants, which transport water from the roots to the leaves. Although largely water, xylem sap contains minute amounts of amino acids, the building blocks from which organisms make proteins, and it is these that spittlebugs use as food. To acquire sufficient amino acids they have to take in copious quantities of xylem sap and excrete most of the water. They can do this because the gut is looped back on itself and water is shunted directly across to the hindgut, leaving a concentrated solution of amino acids in the midgut. As water is discharged from the anus – which happens within a few minutes of them starting to feed – air is pumped into it, so that the nymph becomes surrounded by froth. Of necessity, water is continually excreted, because that is the only way a nymph can get enough food, and conversion of water into enveloping foam prevents desiccation and probably affords some protection from predators. I have never seen birds or predatory insects probing cuckoo-spit for food, but there are some species of wasps which are known to recognize it as the site of prey, and parasitic flies lay eggs in the foam, their larvae developing in the nymphs. As they grow, nymphs moult their skin five times, normally remaining in the mass of foam as they do so. They may move around on plants when disturbed, or to seek out growing shoots, which are easier to penetrate, and where more amino acids are likely to be available, and quickly reconstitute their frothy covering. The nymph stage lasts from five to eight weeks, the rate of development being faster in warmer weather, and when growth is complete, feeding stops and the foam dries, forming a kind of chamber from which the new adult crawls leaving a neat little hole.

Although, in some areas, nymphs of other species of spittlebug are found on grasses and trees, *Philaenus spumarius* has been recorded on more than 400 species of plants, most of them non-woody, in Europe, Asia and North America. It is the only spittlebug in my garden, where I have found cuckoo-spit on 130 species of 47 families, including native and introduced species, a fern, lilies, woody plants such as tamarisk, privet, poplar and ash, and aromatic plants such as tarragon, lavender and rosemary. They are probably able to use such a wide range of different sorts of plants because they feed on watery xylem sap. Most unpalatable or toxic plant chemicals are concentrated in the leaves and other tissues. Although spittlebugs fare better on young shoots, it is evident that their opportunities for feeding are almost unlimited. Consequently their numbers often build up to plague proportions, particularly on clover and lucerne fields, where their siphoning of amino acids from plants reduces growth and crop yield. Population density is usually low in gardens, and there is rarely more than one spittlebug to a plant, so that their effects on growth are negligible. They do, however, seem to have a predilection for rosemary and lavender, and I was a trifle disconcerted to find 13 blobs of cuckoo-spit on a prized young rosemary bush less than a metre in height. Adults do not usually move far, unless plants become too tough for them to penetrate, or they are disturbed by crop harvesting. They may then undertake long-distance movements, so that large numbers appear suddenly in places where there were previously few, and it is possible that garden populations are constantly replenished from the countryside.

Finding and recognizing plants as food

Spittlebugs are such catholic feeders that nymphs have to do little more than find an actively growing green plant – almost any plant will do. By comparison, most herbivorous insects have a restricted diet, and many are confined to one or a few similar species. Immature insects are flightless, and many are relatively immobile and helpless; the onus is on egg-laying females to locate and recognize appropriate foodplants, and some species of butterflies do this visually. But most adult insects, both those that themselves eat plants and those with herbivorous larvae, can detect from considerable distances the characteristic odours of plants, including those that we cannot smell at all, by means of batteries of microscopic sense organs on the antennae. Once an insect has found and alighted on a suitable foodplant, additional information received through sensory receptors on the mouthparts or legs confirm whether it proceeds to take a bite or lay its eggs. Plant-feeding adults, such as flea beetles, and larvae, such as caterpillars, respond to chemical stimuli they receive from a sample bite by either continuing to feed or moving elsewhere.

Many chemical substances found in plants, including those which make lavender or tomatoes so aromatic, play no part in a plant's life processes, and are sometimes called secondary plant substances. To a greater or lesser extent, they are poisonous to insects, and have probably evolved as deterrents to herbivores. However, evolutionary competition between eater and eaten is a continuous process, and development of deterrents by potential food to avoid being eaten, leads inevitably to adaptations for overcoming these defences. Far from being deterred by secondary plant substances, herbivorous insects use them as signals and labels for identifying food. For example, cabbages and related plants are unpalatable to many insects because they contain mustard oils, but these act as attractants for certain species of aphids and flea beetles, and for egg-laying cabbage white butterflies, and also as feeding stimulants. The digestive and metabolic processes of insects restricted to a narrow range of foodplants are adapted to the particular chemistry of the plants they eat, and can cope with toxic constituents of their food.

It is fairly easy to understand how a specialist feeder could have evolved the chemistry to cope with 'poisons', but the situation of insects with a varied diet, known as polyphages, is rather different. Spittlebugs manage because they feed on watery xylem sap, but what of insects which chew leaves? In my garden, for instance, I have found caterpillars of angle shades on 26 plant species, and those of cabbage moths on 31. The plants in the diet of these and other polyphagous moth species are so diverse that there can be no question of chemical similarities between them. Recent work in America on a species of army-worm, moth caterpillars which are notorious pests, suggests how polyphagous moths cope with their varied diet. When an army-worm moves on to a new plant species, the first few mouthfuls trigger production of all-purpose enzymes which break down and neutralize toxic chemicals. The caterpillar becomes in effect immunized against any nasty component in its new food, and thereafter can eat it with impunity. Caterpillars of garden moths which eat a variety of unrelated sorts of plants must have the same sort of adaptable body chemistry.

Buddleia was first introduced to England at the end of the nineteenth century and has been widespread and abundant for less than fifty years. It was brought from China, and belongs to a plant family unrepresented in western Europe, but caterpillars of the holly blue butterfly and of 23 species of moth, including angle shades and cabbage moth, now use it as a foodplant. Most are polyphagous species for which buddleia is just another sort of plant, and we would not expect them to experience difficulties with it. One, however, the mullein moth, is a specialist feeder, previously restricted to mulleins and figworts, both of which belong to the plant family Scrophulariaceae. Buddleia happens to contain a similar secondary plant substance to that found in members of the family Scrophulariaceae. The mullein moth has apparently adopted buddleia as a foodplant because the chemical signal and label are right.

There is obviously far more to the composition of a plant than we humans can detect using only our own senses rather than techniques of chemical analysis. Not only does each species have its characteristic odour, but different branches or groups of branches on an individual of a long-lived plant differ in chemical composition. A tree may be, in effect, a chemical mosaic, which means that a particular species of herbivore is unlikely to be able to use the entire plant, being adapted to only a piece of the mosaic. One consequence is that a given species of caterpillar, aphid, or some other herbivore tends to be clumped on part of a tree. The advantage of such an arrangement to the tree may be considerable, because clumped herbivores are likely to be more obvious to predators. By concentrating its herbivores in one place, a tree makes it easier for a predator to find and remove them all.

Marigolds among the cabbages

An understanding of how plant-feeders find food, and what stimulates them to eat, may seem far removed from gardening, but it can be used to combat the activities of insects that are potential pests of crops. Given that most insects locate their foodplants by smell, it follows that individual herbivores are more likely to be attracted by the massive sensory input they receive from a uniform stand of one sort of plant (a monoculture) and that once there, the stimulus to feed will be maximal. The converse should also be true: that a battery of different scents confuses herbivores so that they have greater difficulty finding food, and feed less efficiently. If this is so, inter-planting susceptible crop plants, not only with different sorts of vegetables, but also with flowers and herbs, should minimize pest damage. Not that there is anything original about this approach. Have you never wondered why old-fashioned cottage gardens have a fine jumble of vegetables, herbs and flowers? Even in grand medieval gardens, like those surrounding the Château Villandry in France, vegetables were inter-planted with ornamental flowers. In the last twenty years or so, there has been a revival of interest in the idea of companion planting, whose adherents believe that certain plant combinations are mutually beneficial. Companion planting has become something of a cult, and there is little factual basis for many beliefs, such as that some plants 'invigorate' the atmosphere for others, but the idea that certain plants give others a measure of protection from pests has to be taken seriously. Almost certainly cottage gardeners and those who originally planned the Château Villandry garden had discovered by trial and error that inter-cropping was more successful than monocultures.

There have been many attempts to put the presumed effectiveness of inter-cropping on a sound scientific footing, although the experimental results are often conflicting. Ecologists working at Cornell University, U.S.A. demonstrated that monocultures of collards (a sort of cabbage) were colonized more rapidly by flea beetles, and suffered more feeding damage, than when they were inter-planted with tomatoes and tobacco. They also showed that the aromatic leaves of tomato and ragweed (*Ambrosia artemisiifolia*) disorient captive flea beetles, so that they have difficulty finding food and seem disinclined to feed. In Russia, tomatoes, potatoes and maize suffer less damage from root-feeding mole crickets when interplanted with hemp. On the other hand, there is experimental evidence, also from the United States, that plots of cabbages bordered by French marigolds and sage, actually support more small cabbage white caterpillars than cabbages grown alone, and that French beans suffer more damage from the caterpillars known as cotton boll-worms, when grown in plots bordered by pot marigolds and other aromatic plants. One thing is certain: there is a lively controversy about the effectiveness of inter-cropping. Different investigators have designed their experiments differently, and apparently contradictory results may be a consequence of studying different sorts of insects. Aromatic plants may disorient some adult herbivores, but if their flowers are attractive as feeding sites for egg-laying adults with herbivorous larvae, any advantage may be lost. Trial and error in a particular place, with a particular crop, are probably necessary for finding the best plant combinations for minimizing insect damage.

I am convinced by the arguments for inter-cropping, and so I mix vegetables, herbs and flowers in my garden. Apart from anything else, the contrast of form, colour and leaf texture looks pleasing, and I do not mind the slight inconvenience in harvesting scattered crop plants, because I enjoy pottering about and taking my time in the garden. True, I quite often need to pick caterpillars from cabbage leaves or peas when preparing vegetables for dinner, but there is still more than enough to eat, and so I have no difficulty in sharing my plants with insects. An increasing number of gardeners find inter-cropping an attractive alternative to the use of chemicals: gardening journals and seed catalogues now advocate sowing basil and French marigolds alongside tomatoes to repel pests, and also inter-planting brassica crops with tomatoes.

Another aspect of mixed planting that deserves consideration is its possibilities for encouraging natural predators of potential pests. Most abundant garden hoverflies, including *Platycheirus, Melanostoma*, and all the familiar medium-sized species banded or spotted with yellow, feed as larvae on aphids, but the adults are flower-feeders. Gravid females are attracted to aggregations of aphids, amongst which they deposit their eggs, not in batches, but singly so that competition for food between members of a brood is minimized. Provision of suitable flat, open flowers, at which female hoverflies can feed, near to plants susceptible to aphid infestation thus increases the chances of eggs being laid amongst the aphids, which will then be eaten by hoverfly larvae. This is an additional reason why I interplant my cabbages, beans and other crops with marigolds, asters and *Rudbeckia*. But it is not only vegetables that are affected by aphids; roses, columbines, nasturtiums and a host of other ornamentals can be disfigured and stunted by massive infestations. Flower beds can also be planned to attract hoverflies and thus ensure maximum consumption of aphids by predatory larvae. The yellow flowers of shrubby cinquefoil are especially attractive to hoverflies, so why not grow this pleasing shrub in the rose garden? Its tiny green leaves and spreading growth contrast well with the large, purple-tinted leaves and stout stems of roses.

A place for weeds

Provision of shelter for predators is just as important as inter-cropping in controlling potential pests, and this is why I have repeatedly urged the advantages of maintaining continuous soil cover. There is a place for so-called weeds in every garden. Ground beetles, spiders, centipedes and other predatory invertebrates need shelter at ground level by day; by night they go hunting for caterpillars and other slow-moving herbivores, often climbing plants to catch their prey. If crops are grown in bare, carefully weeded soil, there is nowhere for predators to shelter by day. There is experimental evidence that this is so; small cabbage white caterpillars on Brussels sprouts suffered significantly more mortality in weedy plots than in hoed plots or those treated with herbicide, because there was a greater abundance of ground beetles in the weedy plots.

PLATE 5 9 The flight path across the garden of many insects brings them up against the lefthand side of the Malaise trap; those that miss it, turn and fly along the herbaceous border (see p. 64). Broom and lilac have to be cut back, periodically, as they tend to shade and obstruct the trap.

As with inter-cropping, however, there are many factors to consider when advocating tolerance of weeds. In the experiments with Brussels sprouts, crop yield was better on hoed than on weedy plots, presumably because there was less competition for soil nutrients, but was actually reduced on plots treated with herbicide. The explanation given for this unexpected result is that a few weed species recovered quickly from the effects of the herbicide used, and then grew rapidly, completely swamping the Brussels sprouts. A balance has to be struck between availability of nutrients for the crop and provision of shelter for predators. Vegetables grown on bare soil will yield well, but there is always risk of massive losses to an opportunist pest species. Insecticides may actually increase problems with those herbivores, such as the caterpillars of small cabbage whites and cabbage moths, which hide deep within the plant 'heart'; they are protected by the leaves from insecticidal sprays, but their predators are particularly susceptible to poisons, and may take some time to re-establish themselves.

The usual concept of a weed is subjective – it is a plant growing in the wrong place. A cabbage plant is my lawn would be a weed, and I usually treat as weeds grass in my vegetable patch. By definition, however, I have few weeds. I like to see hairy bitter-cress, pearlwort and thyme-leaved speedwell in the cracks of my paths, and tolerate many plants that other gardeners regard as weeds in the interests of maintaining good ground cover around the cabbages and other vegetables. On the other hand, self-seeded pot marigolds and evening primroses would swamp my lettuces and radishes if I did not thin them drastically; in the context of the vegetable garden, they become weeds. The answer seems to be occasional hoeing, and selective removal of especially vigorous weeds, whether oxalis and hedge bindweed, or marigolds and evening primroses. Dense vegetation provides shelter, and the richer the animal community in the vegetable garden or elsewhere, the more likely there is to be equilibrium between predators and prey, so that no one species gets out of hand.

A garden geography lesson
Garden floras are distinctive and unusual because so many of the plants cultivated are aliens. This is as true of gardens in Africa, Asia, the Americas and Australia as of those in western Europe. In addition to alien species, many cultivars are grown, leading to considerable confu-

PLATE 6   10 I pick and eat most of the clusters of flower buds on sprouting broccoli, but those I miss develop into sprays of flowers that attract bees and butterflies. 11 Spotted dead-nettle sprawls beneath the raspberry canes. Its purple or white flowers attract bumblebees, and the leaves provide shelter for beetles and other predatory animals (see p. 88).

sion and difficulty when it comes to naming garden plants. A number of wild flowers, such as shrubby cinque-foil and foxgloves, are cultivated in English gardens, often as 'improved' varieties, but the majority are present as 'weeds' and tend to be eliminated. There are only 35 species of trees native to the British Isles, and many of them are intentionally grown in gardens, but the vast majority of familiar trees have been introduced from elsewhere in the world, some of the introductions being very old. On a walk around suburban gardens and parks, you may see more than 500 species, and if large arboreta and collections are included, the tree species list rises to about 1700. In my garden are native birch, elm, holly, hawthorn, apple and rowan, but I also have sycamore, native to central and southern Europe and probably brought by the Romans, and horse chestnut, introduced from Albania and Greece about 1600, as well as more recent introductions, such as Lawson's cypress from western USA, a double flowering cherry from Japan, a purple-leaved form of Myrobalan plum from Persia, and the slender variety of poplar, known as Lombardy poplar, from Italy.

The taxonomic variety of a garden is far higher than that of a natural plant community because of gardeners' predilection for high plant diversity and for alien plants, some of which struggle to survive in our climate. E. J. Salisbury put this succinctly in *The Living Garden*, published in 1935: [Gardens] 'comprise an artificial assemblage of many kinds of plants, the nature and numbers of which are mainly dependent on our arbitrary whims and fancies. Some that we grow are only too patently unfitted for the conditions in which they live, and many more fail to produce offspring and so when they perish must perforce be replaced by artificial propagation or by importation. The plants of a garden grow not where they will but where they must.' Despite this, many introductions thrive and are a familiar part of the garden scene everywhere.

My garden flora includes at least 16 species, including spotted dead-nettle, from northern continental Europe, and more than 40, including lavender, marjoram, sage, rosemary, thyme, borage and other herbs, from southern Europe. A vast array of familiar herbaceous border plants and a number of weeds are native to North America, where lupins, Michaelmas daisies, *Rudbeckia*, goldenrod, sunflowers, *Helenium* and *Heliopsis* brighten meadows and road verges. Other species, including crocuses, mock orange, *Arabis caucasica*, garden peas, lovage and opium poppies, come from southwest Asia; buddleia, pink stonecrop (*Sedum spectabile*) and clematis originate in China, hydrangeas and privet in Japan, and hollyhocks, chrysanthemums and asters grow in both countries. Chile is represented by *Berberis darwinii* and Chilean potato tree, Siberia by tarragon, rhubarb and pineappleweed (*Matricaria matricarioides*), the Himalayas by Himalayan honeysuckle (*Leycesteria formosa*), and the Canary Islands by marguerite daisies (*Chrysanthemum frutescens*) and a shrubby *Hypericum*. Hotter parts of the world are represented by smaller numbers of species; these can only be grown in summer, and some barely survive other than in warm years, although they include an amazing number of vegetables. Dahlias, Mexican orange blossom, *Tagetes* and *Cosmos bipinnatus* come from Mexico, nasturtiums from Peru, red *Salvia splendens* and nicotiana from Brazil, and a dozen other species from Central or South America, including runner beans, marrows, sweet peppers, tomatoes, petunias, thorn-apples (*Datura*) and the passion flower (*Passiflora caerulea*). To complete the geographical spectrum, there is basil from India, aubergines and balsam from southeastern Asia, melons from tropical Africa, *Lobelia erinus*, *Agapanthus* lilies and the lawn 'moss' or buttonweed (*Cotula coronopifolia*) from South Africa, and the 'marvel of Peru' (*Mirabilis jalapa*) from the West Indies.

Most of these aliens from far-flung parts of the world are intentionally cultivated garden plants, although a few were accidentally introduced, have become naturalized, and are usually classed as weeds. If we add to these all the native plants that come into a garden of their own accord, it becomes obvious that gardening creates an extraordinarily rich flora, which provides food, whether leaves, flowers, fruit or seeds, for a multitude of different animals. It is curious that the rich fauna of gardens depends on one of their features that ecologists condemn as artificial, namely the collecting together of plants from every corner of the world.

A good catch

The light trap (see p. 100) is still bringing in spring species of moths, such as the common quaker, the Hebrew character, the early grey and the brindled beauty, but the character of the catch is changing, with increasing numbers of the bright-line brown-eye and the heart and dart, whose names graphically describe the markings on their wings. Welcome harbingers of summer are the first hawk moths, although few individuals and only two species are normally trapped so early in the season. The poplar hawk is a soft grey colour, sometimes pinkish in the female, with a dull red patch at the base of each hind wing; its caterpillars, green with oblique yellow stripes on the sides and a red-tipped 'horn' at the rear, feed on poplars and willows, and can sometimes be found even on solitary poplars in inner city gardens. The lime hawk is an elegant and beautiful moth, the fore wings terracotta coloured with large moss-green markings, and the antennae and legs bright pinkish-brown; the green caterpillars, with oblique side stripes of yellow and reddish-purple, and a yellow-tipped, blue 'horn' at the rear, feed on elm and limes. Built for fast flight, with stream-lined wings, hawk moths seem large and exotic beside the drab, brownish moths that make up the bulk of the catch. Four species are quite common, but being nocturnal are rarely seen so that the occasional individual surprised by day resting on a fence is often taken for a rarity.

All eight species of garden bumblebees enter the Malaise trap, not only fat, over-wintered queens, but also, towards the end of the month, the first workers. Single individuals of two species of cuckoo bumble-bees have also been trapped in May: *Psithyrus vestalis* resembles *Bombus terrestris*, whose nests it takes over, and *P. rupestris* is black with a red tail, like its host *B. lapidarius*. There are three species of large, fat black bees with red tails in the garden, but it is not difficult to tell them apart as they feed at flowers. Have no fear of approaching your nose to within an inch or two of a bumblebee, for they are docile creatures and rarely use their stings. In bumblebees, the second long section, or tibia, of the hind legs is expanded, and flattened or slightly concave on the side away from the body, and long hairs curve inwards over its smooth, shiny surface, to form a pollen basket; in *B. lapidarius*, the incurved hairs are black, but in *B. ruderarius* they are red. It is only females that have pollen baskets, but most bumblebees seen at flowers are females. Female cuckoo bees, however, have no pollen baskets, the hind tibia being convex and uniformly hairy like the rest of the legs, and the hard cuticle shows through their sparse hair. In May the Malaise trap also catches solitary bees, a few honeybees, queen wasps, and perhaps the first *Vespula germanica* workers. The exact composition of the catch varies enormous-ly from year to year, depending on the weather and how advanced the season is. In a warm, sunny May, there may be several ladybirds, mostly the familiar red 2-spot, perhaps an over-wintered 7-spot, one or two black- and yellow-checkered 14-spot, and a few 10-spot ladybirds, the latter needing careful identification as they are so variable in colour and pattern.

The hoverfly sample bears out garden observations, consisting largely of slim, dark *Platycheirus* and *Melanostoma*, with a reasonable number of black- and yellow-banded *Syrphus ribesii*, and of *Epistrophe eligans* in warmer years. *E.eligans*, black with restricted yellow markings on the base of the abdomen, is quite abundant in May and June, but never occurs later in the season. It is one of the garden species characteristic of open places, and is most often seen hovering in sunlight above the lawn. Forty-seven species of hoverflies have turned up in May catches, many more than I am aware of seeing in the garden. Some are inconspicuous, shade-frequenting species like the curiously elongate and slender *Baccha elongata*; others are rare garden visitors represented by only one or two individuals in the total ten-year catch, and these include woodland species, such as robust, fluffy *Criorhina floccosa*, whose larvae feed on decaying material in rot-holes in trees. It is an encouraging sign when a fair proportion of May trap samples consists of species typical of summer rather than spring. *Rhingia campestris*, a yellowish, globular fly, is instantly recognizable by its peculiarly prominent upper mouth edge on which the mouthparts are mounted; with this arrangement it can suck nectar from tubular flowers too deep for most hoverflies. *Rhingia* larvae develop in and feed on cow-pats, and adults, like those of woodland species, are evidently visiting gardens in quest of nectar. Few of the hoverflies caught are so distinctive, and it has taken many hours of concentrated work with a microscope to establish, for instance, that eight species of *Platycheirus* occur in May, and to sort out the numerous species with yellow bands or paired spots on a black abdomen. Early in the summer, I have to refresh my memory repeatedly from books or my reference collection of named species, but as the summer progresses, I 'get my eye in' and identification becomes easier. The May list of hoverflies tells me a great deal about seasonal feeding opportunities in the garden: most of the species caught have rather short tongues and aphid-feeding larvae, whereas late summer species tend to have longer tongues, making different sorts of flowers accessible, and many more have larvae that feed on decaying material. Thus the catch indicates that many flat, open flowers bloom early in summer, that aphids quickly become available as a productive food source, and that decomposing material is more plentiful later in the year.

6

JUNE

Moth watch

A sprinkling of yellow flower-heads of buttonweed, each one like a diminutive fleshy pincushion stuck with tiny, tubular florets, is a reminder that the grass needs cutting again, but for the time being I am content to sit back in the sun and contemplate my surroundings. Broken wings strewn on the grass show where a bird has caught a small cabbage white butterfly and eaten the body, and a blackbird is diligently collecting caterpillars of large cabbage whites from the broccoli for its brood. The yellow and black caterpillars aggregate on exposed parts of plants, and are generally assumed to be distasteful, but this particular blackbird seems undeterred. A house martin darts unerringly beneath the eaves of a neighbouring house to make an addition to the nest it is plastering against the wall. Thrushes are feeding spotty fledglings, and a pair of greenfinches keep disappearing with beakfuls of food into the mock orange where they have a nest. Redpolls fly over continually, making sibilant twittering calls; a hedge sparrow is singing from the top of a holly tree, its melodious song at odds with its drab plumage, and snatches of willow warbler song come from a neighbouring garden. Newly arrived willow warblers sing in the garden in spring, but hitherto have always moved elsewhere to breed. They nest on the ground amongst dense vegetation, and so suburban gardens are not a particularly good habitat for them, but continuous song so late in the season certainly suggests that this year they are breeding locally.

As I laze in the sun, I get a better overall view of the garden than when I am toiling head down, and I cannot help but wonder why the garden pea plants on the other side of the fence in my neighbour's garden are taller and lusher than mine! Still, as long as they yield peas, does it really matter? The raspberries are coming along nicely, and it is about time I erected the netting cage over them. I have learnt by experience not to cover them too early, because then canes grow through the netting and get damaged every time it is lifted for picking. So often recently early June has been wet: a mixed blessing, for although raspberries are plump, gooseberries mildew and strawberries rot on the plants long before they are ripe.

The planned mixed planting of the lawn bed has been predictably augmented by a host of self-sown evening primroses and pot marigolds, and, rather unexpectedly, by three healthy seedlings of nicotiana, which seem to be doing far better than those grown in boxes from seed carefully collected from last year's plants. The lawn bed is always a pot-pourri of surprises, not the least being the red-legged partridge I flushed from among the lettuces early one morning. Feverfew is thriving here as everywhere else in the garden; at first the plants are attractive with their divided yellowish-green leaves, although later on they become straggly and smothered with black aphids. Bees are reputed to dislike the composite flowers, yellow at the centre, surrounded by white ray-florets, and certainly I have no recollection of seeing bees on the flowers, although flies visit them. The entire plant is strongly aromatic, smelling a bit like camphor, and this is one of the self-sowing garden species that I am quite happy to see growing amongst vegetables susceptible to insect damage. An infusion of flower-heads is a traditional country insect repellent, and it is an old medicinal herb, used particularly as a febrifuge – hence its English name. Recent research has shown that its action is similar to that of aspirin, which is probably why it is considered effective for relieving migraine. The scientific name, *Tanacetum parthenium*, refers to its putative use to save the life of a workman who fell from the Parthenon while it was being built. Whether or not the story is true, feverfew has long been regarded as lucky, and was once planted near houses to purify the air and keep diseases at bay.

A closer look

I can see enough from my deck-chair to whet my curiosity. So it is time to stretch my legs and take a look at what else is happening in the garden. The teasel plants have shot up to shoulder height, and the cups formed by the clasping bases of their leaves are full of water. This acts as a barrier to ants that might rob the flowers of nectar, and now the pools are murky with the decomposing bodies of drowned insects. It is probable that the plant absorbs some of the nutrients released as the corpses decay, which may be why teasels shoot up so quickly, even in poor soil.

For the second day running, I remove a large, healthy-looking garden snail (*Helix aspersa*) from the cold frame; I put the one found yesterday at least ten metres away. Could it have crept back again? A blackbird has been rootling amongs mats of white stonecrop, leaving the tiny, cylindrical leaves scattered all over the path, where each that falls into a crack will no doubt sprout into a new plant. The path flora is becoming more attractive, with green cushions of thyme-leaved speedwell putting up spikes of delicate white flowers veined with purple. I surprise a couple of shiny, damp smooth newts, olive-brown above and orange beneath, in the cool shade under the perennial candytuft that overhangs a path near the old pond. In the drought year, my heavy clay soil cracked, and the pond sprang a leak; as fast as I filled it, the water seeped away. One side of the pond is formed by a densely planted rockery, close to a bay of the house; locating, let alone patching, the leak would have involved a major upheaval, so the pond has remained dry. But every year, the newts return.

Woody nightshade, or bittersweet, curtains the holly and Lawson's cypresses on the east side of the front garden; I weed it from other places, but the drapery softens the starkness of the evergreen, and its purple flowers and bright red berries add welcome touches of colour. Tiny, brown beetles have chewed small, clean-edged holes in the leaves, and while searching for the culprits my attention is drawn to an amorphous blob hanging in a flimsy network of threads. As its shape changes, I realize that it is a seething mass of tiny, newly-hatched spiders. Yellow with a large black mark on the abdomen, they are almost certainly garden spiders (*Araneus diadematus*), which construct the familiar orb-webs later in the summer. Females lay eggs in clusters, and for the first day or so after hatching, the babies remain in a ball, feeding on their eggshells (and to some extent on each other). After a couple of days they disperse, and careful searching is needed to find even one, sheltering beneath a leaf.

A female orange-tip butterfly, captured and confined in a netting bag on the green pods of an ordinary cabbage that had been allowed to go to seed, laid one egg that has hatched into a bluish-green caterpillar. Cabbages are rarely allowed to go to seed, so are not usually available as a food source, but the solitary caterpillar seems to be doing quite well. Chewed leaves on gooseberry and flowering currant bushes are easily traced to conspicuous caterpillars, white and yellow with rows of black blotches and dots. These belong to the magpie moth, which will be on the wing at night later in the month. The colours and pattern of the moth's wings are very similar to those of the caterpillars, and they are equally striking.

On the path is a moribund queen bumblebee, the third, of three different species, that I have found dead, or apparently dying, in the last few days. It is not clear what has happened to them, although one had its sting extruded. It may be that they have been evicted from their nests by cuckoo bees, for this is the time of year when they move in to established nests and take them over. Bumblebee numbers are now at their peak in Malaise trap samples, as nests of all the garden species are going concerns, with active complements of workers. There is an empty blackbird's nest in the broom bush from which four young have flown. I lift it down to look at its construction more closely, and realize that it is crawling with larvae of nest flies (*Neottiophilum praeustum*). The flies lay their eggs in occupied nests, and the resulting larvae suck the blood of nestling birds, eventually pupating in the nest fabric. There are no less than 70 larvae in the nest, enough to constitute a considerable drain on the resources of the baby birds, so it is comforting to know that they have successfully fledged.

The sun sinks, but it is still warm, and an idle afternoon gives way to contemplation of the garden by twilight. The dark mass of the mock orange is strewn with white flowers that seem to glow in the dusk, and the air is fragrant with honeysuckle, whose scent, like that of most moth-pollinated flowers, is strongest in the evening. It is time to move the moth trap on to the lawn, switch on the lamp, and begin the moth watch. The bluish light transforms the garden into a fairyland of unaccustomed gleaming shapes and deep shadows, and silhouettes the delicate tracery of the birch tree against the pale walls of the house. And so we wait, confident as always that some rarity will flit into the circle of light.

The moth and the flame

Moths flutter against lighted window panes, circle street lamps, and singe their wings on candle flames, yet do not fly towards the moon. Indeed, migratory species navigate by the moon and stars, maintaining a preferred compass direction by using them as fixed points. What is it about certain sorts of light that attracts moths? The most attractive, such as mercury vapour discharge tubes and 'black lights', emit large amounts of ultra-violet radiation. We know that ultra-violet is visible to bees and other insects, and so it is widely believed that moths are attracted by ultra-violet. This gets us no nearer understanding the phenomenon, other than to assume that some accident of design of moths' eyes distorts their perception of light and compels them to approach it. Another theory is that moths respond to a candle or electric lamp as they would to the moon. They try to maintain a fixed direction with reference to the artificial light, but since they are close to it, this results in a circular flight path. In other words, conventional explanations concentrate on the way a moth's eyes function. Perhaps, however, they perceive something of which we are unaware, with a sense that we lack; perhaps they are attracted to candles and other lights, because they mistake them for something else.

We owe to an American entomologist a startlingly original yet plausible theory about the perceptual world of moths, which establishes a connection between the ability of male moths to locate a female of the same species over distances of more than a kilometre, and their attraction to light. The essence of the theory is that moths are able to tune in to radiation emitted by scent molecules. They appear to be able to perceive electro-magnetic waves in the infra-red, i.e. of wavelength intermediate between visible light and radio waves, using their antennae to pick up the signals. The pectinate antennae of some male moths are even designed like man-made VHF antennae. Sun, moon, stars, the earth itself, and indeed any object with a temperature above absolute zero $(-273°C)$ emit infra-red radiation, which it is believed, energizes scent molecules so that they fluoresce. The principle is exactly the same as energizing the gas in a neon strip light, with electricity, so that it fluoresces. We can see much of the fluorescence of a strip light, or discharge tube, but that of scent molecules is infra-red and, to us, imperceptible. For a moth, however, the myriad, drifting scent molecules that swirl through the air, are transmitting a range of different signals, as though they were glowing in many different hues – none of which we can perceive at all. Moths tune in to scent molecules, with their sensitive antennae, and thus locate mates and foodplants.

What do fluorescent scent molecules have to do with attraction to light? Candle flames, lighted window panes, electric light bulbs, and, in particular, mercury vapour discharge tubes and 'black lights', emit vast amounts of infra-red radiation. This acts like the energy input to a laser, which 'pumps' molecules of gases or solids so that the electro-magnetic waves they emit are synchronized, which means they are amplified and intensified. The cloud of scent molecules swirling around a candle, window pane, or lamp are irradiated and energized into a state of amplified transmission; from a moth's point of view, it is as though they were illuminated. Attraction, then, is not to the light as such, but to sex attractants and foodplant scents, which have been turned into transmitters by infra-red radiation from the source of light. This explains why a light trap is more effective on a still, moonless night: scent molecules hanging motionless in still air broadcast a continuous, strong message to which a moth can orient; in moonlight, scent molecules will be fluorescing all over the place, but when there is no moon, fluorescence produced by a mercury vapour lamp is a strong, clear beacon against the faint background of fluorescence caused by blackbody radiation from the earth.

I find the theory attractive and plausible, although difficult to comprehend, since I am neither an engineer nor a physicist. It is certainly an improvement on assumptions that moths are forced to approach light, or circle candle flames, because of some quirk in the design of their eyes, or beliefs that male moths locate females over distances of more than a kilometre because of prodigious powers of smell. It also explains the extraordinary branched antennae of some male moths, and the complex system of microscopic sensory rods, pits and discs, revealed by high-power electron microscopy, that cover moth antennae. Admittedly, I find it hard to envisage the air as seething with scent molecules, but this is a sad consequence of the dullness of human sensory abilities. The way in which most animals operate is circumstantial evidence that their perceptual world is largely one of scent. By tuning in to infra-red signals, moths probably experience a world illuminated by swirling, glowing scent molecules.

Whatever the reason for moths flying towards a bright light, it can be exploited as a means of catching them. The most effective is a mercury vapour bulb, which contains gas under pressure; when a current is passed through it, the gas is first ionized, and then fluoresces, emitting ultra-violet and infra-red radiation as well as visible light. The lamp can simply be placed against a white background, such as a sheet hanging from the clothes line. Moths, attracted to the light, settle on the sheet where they can be inspected and identified without handling or catching them. This necessitates sitting by the light for much of the night, which even the keenest moth-watcher is unlikely to want to do, so most people use a light trap. This exploits the way that many moths close their wings and drop when they brush against a light bulb. The socket for the bulb is at the centre of a shallow metal funnel, 30 centimetres in diameter. Four metal baffles project in from the sides of the funnel, increasing the tendency of moths to fall down through the funnel into the main part of

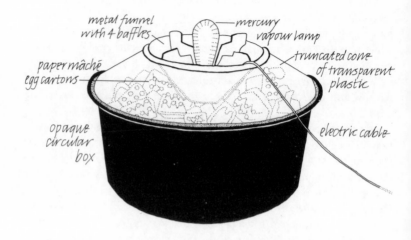

metal funnel
with 4 baffles

mercury
vapour lamp

paper mâché
egg cartons

truncated cone
of transparent
plastic

opaque
circular
box

electric cable

LIGHT TRAP

the trap, which is a circular, black box, 60 centimetres in diameter and 25 centimetres high. Onto this fits a truncated cone of transparent plastic, which surrounds and supports the metal funnel.

The trap box is filled with papier mâché egg-cartons, providing surfaces on which moths can settle and beneath which they can hide, rather than blundering round and round, and damaging themselves. A trap like this can be set up and left unattended all night, and then, next day, the egg-boxes can be unpacked and the catch inspected at leisure. Unpacking the trap is always exciting, for under any egg-box there may be a large hawk moth, or some rarity. Any that cannot be identified immediately are collected for more detailed examination, but the advantage of this trapping method is that collecting, i.e. killing, is kept to an absolute minimum. Most of the catch is released, although not until next evening, after watchful sparrows have gone to roost.

A June moth catch
Numbers are building up towards a peak in August, but the outstanding feature of early summer catches is their variety. One or two moth species, like the bright-line brown-eye and the heart and dart, are fairly numerous, but apart from these, nearly every moth in the trap looks

different from the others. There is the year's first silver Y, so called because of a bright, Y-shaped mark on the fore wings. Although one of the commonest town moths, it is an immigrant from southern Europe, and, like swifts and house martins, flies north to exploit feeding opportunities offered in the English summer. Since 1972, they have arrived in June every year, except in 1976, when many biological events, including the silver Y's arrival, happened a month earlier than usual. Two moths with Y-shaped gilt markings on their wings turn out to be different species, the beautiful golden Y having more marbled fore wings than the plain golden Y. A close relative is the burnished brass, as gleaming as its name suggests, with metallic yellow bands on the fore wings. The uniformly whitish-green wings of a light emerald moth, and the brighter green of a common emerald, look like leaves caught in the trap. The bold markings of a magpie moth contrast with the sombre browns of cabbage, dot and turnip moths, although when disturbed, the latter reveals pale, almost white, hind wings. A flattened, brown moth drops from an egg-box and flutters into the vegetation fringing the lawn, with a flash of golden yellow hind wings – the first large yellow underwing of the season. It is probably the commonest garden moth, and I often find its fat caterpillars and shiny brown pupae when weeding or clearing vegetation.

The catch includes so many different moths, each attractive and interesting in its own way, that it is not easy to know which to single out for special mention. One of the larger ones is the swallow-tailed moth, which has creamy white wings, the hind pair with short, blunt 'tails', each bearing a pair of reddish spots. They belong to the family Geometridae, most of which have caterpillars that progress by a series of loops, as though measuring the ground: hence geometers or ground measurers. Looper caterpillars may be green or brown in colour, and they have a pair of claspers at the rear end, on which they can support themselves so rigidly that they look exactly like a twig or stick. I have found the large, brown, stick-like caterpillars of the swallow-tailed moth feeding on flowering currant and privet. Another conspicuous geomet-rid in the catch, is a brimstone moth, which has bright yellow wings blotched with red. They are common in the garden, where the caterpillars feed on hawthorn, japonica and Myrobalan plum; many of the caterpillars on the Myrobalan plum are quite purple in colour, matching the leaves and young twigs. The largest stick caterpillars in the garden are those of the scalloped hazel, which feeds on a variety of plants, including buddleia, beauty bush, mock orange, spiraea, and Myrobalan plum. Scalloped hazel moths, which vary in colour from pale to dark brown, with scalloped edges to the wings, are often caught in June. Unlike most geometrids, they rest with the wings closed over the back, like a butterfly, looking like a dead leaf.

It is always a delight to find a hawk moth among the catch, perhaps a lime or poplar hawk, and sometimes an exotic-looking elephant hawk moth, olive-green brushed with bright pink; its inapposite name refers to the trunk-like way the caterpillars extend and move their front ends when feeding. The more usual capture is an eyed hawk. The fore wings are camouflaged like dead leaves, and so at rest they are inconspicuous; if disturbed, however, they expose the hind wings, which bear startling, black-ringed blue eye-spots against a vivid pink background. Another handsome capture is a puss moth, its body and legs as softly furry as a white kitten, its pale, downy wings veined with yellow and delicately etched with grey, like watermarks on paper. Their dramatic caterpillars feed on willow and poplar; they are green, with a white-edged, purplish-brown saddle and a forked tail, and when irritated, rear up, draw the head into the hunched 'shoulders' exposing a large, red, false face, and protrude a pair of lashing red threads from the forked tail.

A delta-winged, black moth, in shape like one of those triangular fighter planes, is a melanic form of the peppered moth. A bird dropping turns out to be a Chinese character moth, although I have to look closely to be sure. Each white fore wing bears a slightly iridescent, greyish-brown patch, and, when the wings are held close alongside the body, it looks nothing like a moth. To complete the illusion, if touched, it drops rather than flying. Another white-winged moth, sitting with the wings held close along the sides of the abdomen, is a male ghost moth, so called because of the wraith-like way it sways back and forth through the air at dusk; females are yellowish-brown and not at all ghostly. Another white moth that may appear in June catches, although it is more frequent later in the summer, is the gold-tail, which derives its names from a tuft of golden-yellow hairs at the tip of the abdomen. Females use the hairs, which are irritating to the touch, to cover their egg batches, laid on hawthorn. Caterpillars hibernate while still quite small, and complete their development the following year, sometimes on garden roses. They are striking to look at, coal-black with rows of white and scarlet spots, and covered with long, black, stinging hairs.

The moths I have described are medium-sized to large, but there are also many tiny moths. The pugs are small geometrids, and the catch includes several, among them a common pug, brown and rather undistinguished-looking, and a green pug, more brown than green in colour. The caterpillars of most pugs feed inside flowers and seed-pods, and although many are abundant in gardens, careful searching is needed to find them. Other small moths belong to the group of families known as micro-Lepidoptera; many are difficult to identify, and the majority of books about moths deal only with the more familiar macro-Lepidoptera. The garden pebble is a creamy white streaked with brown; it rests with the wings half folded and the large mouth palps projecting forwards, so that it assumes a sharply-angled V-shape, like a paper dart. It is common in the garden, adding to the load of herbivores my cabbages have to carry; the caterpillars, which are unusual in that they hibernate within silken cocoons in the soil, are minor pests when common, eating out cabbage hearts. Another 'micro', which makes a bright splash of colour in the trap, is the gold fringe, a tiny, pinkish-red moth, its wings spotted and bordered with golden yellow. Since its caterpillars feed on hay, straw, and other dried plant material, it is sometimes assumed to be a country moth, although it is common in my suburban garden.

Pollination of flowers

Tall spikes of purplish-blue sage flowers dominate my garden in June. The scientific name of sage, *Salvia*, comes from the Latin word meaning 'I am well', and the Romans introduced the plant to Britain for use in medicine and cooking. Our medieval ancestors used it lavishly, together with onions, in poultry dishes, so sage and onion stuffing has a long pedigree. Bumblebees come and go incessantly, visiting the hooded flowers to feed, and, in the process, pollinating them. The individual flowers could not be better designed for pollination by bumblebees. The petal that forms the broad lower lip serves as a landing platform, and purple and white striations in the throat guide visitors to the nectaries at the base of the flower tube. The stamens (two of them) are each shaped a bit like a telephone receiver attached by a hinge at the middle; the pollen-bearing anthers at one end lie in the throat of the flower, whereas those at the other end are concealed beneath the upper, hood-shaped petal. As a bee delves into the flower, it pushes against the lower anthers, so that the upper ones swing down in a see-saw action, from within the hood, and strike it on the back, covering it with pollen. In freshly-opened, pollen-producing flowers, the stigma is above the anthers, within the hood, but in older flowers, it curves downwards, and visiting bees brush against it, transferring to it any pollen on their backs.

Bumblebees are the only insects with tongues long enough to reach the nectar, which are also bulky enough to fill the flower entrance, so that they operate the stamen mechanism and brush against the stigma.

Pollination is a necessary prelude to sexual reproduction in flowering plants. Female sex cells, or eggs, are inside the ovaries, which are usually more or less hidden beneath or within a flower. Each ovary bears a projecting style, which terminates in a stigma on which pollen is deposited during pollination. Male sex cells – the equivalent of sperm – are contained in pollen grains. When it lands on a stigma of the same species, a pollen grain begins to grow; a tube develops, penetrates the stigma, grows down the style into the ovary, and enters an egg. The male nucleus (containing genes, the hereditary material) moves along the pollen tube, and so into the egg, where it fuses with the female nucleus, thus accomplishing fertilization. The majority of flowering plants are hermaphrodite: they produce male and female cells on the same individual, normally within the same flower. Sage flowers, for instance, have both ovaries and pollen-producing stamens. Self-pollination would seem sensible and economical, yet plants go to great lengths to ensure cross-pollination. The main disadvantage of self-pollination, and consequent self-fertilization, arises because male and female cells produced by the same individual are likely to carry the same genetic information. The effects of harmful hereditary traits are usually masked by a corresponding trait, but if eggs are fertilized by male cells carrying genes for the same trait, that trait is bound to be expressed in the offspring. Self-pollination is discouraged by the maturing of male and female parts of a flower at different times, or the positioning of the stigma above the stamens and out of the way of falling pollen. In addition, many species are self-incompatible, so that self-pollination does not lead to fertilization. However, self-fertilization is better than leaving no offspring at all, and many plant species have evolved a balance between self- and cross-pollination. The problem is that plants are stationary. They cannot take their sex cells to other individuals in the way that animals do, but have to use external agents. Flowers are simply devices for expediting the transfer of pollen, and the agents most frequently used are wind and insects.

Wind-pollination is used by grasses, conifers, plantains, many of our commonest trees such as oak and ash, and a variety of other plants. It is a haphazard process, depending for success on production of enormous quantities of pollen – to the disadvantage of hay-fever sufferers. Each of the tiny florets that makes up a flowering spike of rye produces over

50,000 pollen grains, and a single birch catkin produces about five-and-a-half-million. So much pollen is produced that stigmas close to ripe stamens would become smothered, to the exclusion of pollen from other individuals; this is avoided by separating stamens and stigma in time (maturing out of phase with each other) or in space (being borne in different flowers or on different plants). The stamens and stigmas of wind-pollinated flowers are large and well exposed, to facilitate liberation and interception of pollen, but petals and sepals are reduced or absent.

The first flower visitors, in the evolutionary sense, were probably pollen-feeding beetles, although a number of different sorts of insects feed on pollen. Some species of beetles, hoverflies and bees visit wind-pollinated flowers to eat pollen, or in the case of bees to collect it for their larvae, and inevitably contribute to transfer of pollen from flower to flower. Plants have capitalized on this activity by evolving colourful, fragrant, nectar-producing flowers. Neither nectar, showy petals, nor sweet scents serve any function in a plant's life processes: nectar is simply bait for insects or, in some tropical flowers, for birds or bats; conspicuous petals and perfumes are labels that advertise the whereabouts of nectar and attract insects to it. The pollen of insect-pollinated flowers is sticky; insect visitors inadvertently pick it up on their heads, bodies, legs, wings or mouthparts, so transferring it to other flowers. This leads to pollination because individual nectar-feeding insects tend to be consistent, in the short term, to a particular species of flower. Some flowers are visited by a wide range of different types of insects; the structure of others is adapted to particular sorts of pollinators. Sage is a good example of a bumblebee flower, designed in such a way that a bee lands and approaches the nectar by a route that ensures contact with stamens or stigma.

For most of the summer, bumblebees are the most conspicuous garden animals, and they are the main pollinators of many garden flowers. The largest bumblebees can get right inside foxgloves, so that only intermittent, high-pitched buzzing betrays their presence, and perhaps this gave rise to the name of the flower. 'Fox' is a corruption of 'folks', implying that they belong to the fairies, and *gleow* is the Anglo-Saxon name for a musical instrument incorporating a row of bells. The bell-shaped flowers have a conspicuous landing platform, liberally speckled with white-ringed, dark purple markings that guide a bee to the nectaries at the base of the petal tube. White foxgloves appear to have only a few brownish speckles, but they probably have nectar-guides that reflect ultra-violet. The spectrum of light visible to bees is shifted towards the shorter wavelengths; they see ultra-violet, but not red. When photographed with special film sensitive to ultra-violet, many flowers prove to have nectar-guides which would be conspicuous to bees, although invisible to the human eye. The floral mechanism of foxgloves favours cross-pollination. The stigma and stamens of newly opened flowers fit snugly against the upper part of the bell, and the anther lobes are pressed together, preventing release of the fine pollen. As a bee delves into a flower for nectar, and presses against the stamen bases, the anther lobes separate, showering pollen onto the visitor. In older flowers, the stamens are well separated, and curve round the sides of the bell, while the central style bends downwards so that its stigma brushes the back of entering bees.

The white-tailed bumblebees, *Bombus hortorum* and *B.ruderatus*, have the longest tongues, almost equal in length to their bodies, and these have no trouble with deep, narrow flowers like comfrey and columbines, but others, such as *B.terrestris*, have tongues only half as long as their bodies. Short-tongued bumblebees often bite a small, circular hole in the base of comfrey flowers and steal the nectar. Such illegitimate entry to a flower, bypassing the stamens and stigma, constitutes theft, since nectar has evolved as bait for insects which pollinate a flower when they enter in the conventional way.

Not all flowers are as specialized as sage or foxgloves in their pollination mechanisms, or call for insects with such long tongues. The nectar of buttercups is only partially concealed beneath a flap at the base of the petals, and it can be reached by short-tongued insects. Beetles, flies, bees, moths, bugs and thrips visit the flowers, some for pollen rather than nectar. Buttercups are self-incompatible, and the stigmas become receptive before the stamens shed their pollen. The flowers of shrubby cinquefoil, another June flower, are superficially similar in shape and colour, but flowers are functionally male, with only rudimentary styles, or functionally female, with rudimentary stamens. They are particularly attractive to hoverflies, which eat both nectar and pollen. Hoverflies tend to inspect any bright yellow object, which is why they settle indiscriminately on yellow shirts, dresses or garden furniture.

Nectar in rowan flowers is completely exposed and accessible; individual flowers are small, but they are massed into conspicuous flat, open bunches, or umbels, over which insects can walk at random. The situation is somewhat similar in daisies and other members of the family

Compositae; 'flowers' are really flower-heads, composed of a tight cluster of small florets. In the daisy type, a mass of tubular disc-florets is surrounded by an outer ring of ray-florets, usually of a contrasting colour, each with a petal-like extension on one side; the dandelion type are composed entirely of ray-florets; and a few, such as tansy, entirely of disc-florets. Individual florets of many composite flowers are shallow, and their nectar can be reached by short-tongued insects, such as beetles and flies, but cornflowers and thistles have deep florets, and are visited by long-tongued bees and butterflies. The conspicuous, feathery, blue florets of perennial cornflower (*Centaurea montana*) are sterile, but the functional pink florets incorporate a curious mechanism for facilitating pollen transfer. The prominent black anthers are fused into a tube within which pollen is liberated; as the style grows up the tube it pushes pollen out of the end. The stamens are sensitive and contract when touched, with the result that the style acts like a piston, and forces a dollop of pollen out of the tube onto a visiting insect.

Butterfly and moth flowers, such as valerian, nicotiana, and various sorts of *Phlox* and *Dianthus*, are more restricted in their clientele than bee flowers, because their petal tubes are too deep and narrow for anything other than a long, thin proboscis. Unlike bees, flies and beetles, British butterflies visit flowers only for nectar, although there are South American species that use pollen for food as well. Most insects can use a greater range of flowers than those specially adapted for their visits; butterflies and moths visit many flowers with quite short flower tubes and easily accessible nectar, being particularly partial to buddleia, the 'butterfly bush'. Like bees, they may be remarkably opportunist in their feeding. I watched a small cabbage white feeding at the pale yellow flowers of a broccoli spray. Some of the flowers were wide open, others were still closed, the incurved petals blocking the end of the tube. The butterfly started at the bottom of the spike of flowers, approaching each conventionally from the front, but as it worked up, and reached the closed flowers, it unhesitatingly switched to a side approach, inserting its proboscis between the bases of petals and sepals to reach the nectaries at the bottom of the flower tube. When a butterfly behaves like this, it is cheating the plant, for there is no chance of it brushing its scaly head and body against stamens or stigma, and no way in which it can effect pollination. Although not so important as furry bees, there is no doubt that butterflies do transfer pollen from flower to flower, and I remember watching, in my West African garden, a swallowtail butterfly so smothered with pollen that its black and yellow pattern was almost obliterated. In temperate climates, however, moths are more important than butterflies as pollinators.

Many pale, fragrant flowers with long petal tubes open in the evening, when moths are first on the wing looking for food; nicotiana and honeysuckle seem to glow in the half-light, and their scents seem particularly strong. Not only are moth flowers more attractive in the evening, but their production of nectar also reaches a peak. Although honeysuckle is specially adapted for pollination by nocturnal hawk moths, the most important pollinator is probably the silver Y moth, and it is also visited by day by hummingbird hawk moths. Some experimental work has suggested that moths use sight rather than scent to locate flowers, but the heavy perfumes of pale, long-tubed flowers that open in the evening imply the contrary. The elegant flowers of turk's cap lilies and madonna lilies are pollinated by hawk moths, whose wings brush against the projecting stamens and stigma as they hover in front of flowers sucking up nectar with their long probosces. Hedge bindweed, however, is something of a puzzle. It is tempting to assume that its large, white, trumpet-shaped flowers are pollinated by crepuscular hawk moths. But the flowers open soon after sunrise, and, by mid-morning on a sunny day, bees and hoverflies have removed the pollen.

Some tentative generalizations are possible about flowers and their insect pollinators. Insects with short to medium-length tongues, such as hoverflies and short-tongued bees, favour white and yellow flowers; these usually have exposed or only partially concealed nectar, and abundant pollen. Blue and purple flowers tend to have fully concealed nectar, and are visited by long-tongued bees. Some species of butterflies favour yellow flowers, some prefer blue or purple, and many visit red or pinkish flowers, which tend to have narrow, deep petal tubes; many tropical butterfly flowers are red. In spring and early summer, when flies and short-tongued bees are abundant, flowers are predominantly white or yellow; later in the season, when there are more long-tongued bees and butterflies about, there are more blue, purple and red flowers. Flowers depend on bees and other insects for pollination; butterflies, moths, bees, hoverflies and a host of other insects depend on flowers for food. Flowers and their pollinators are mutually dependent, and neither could exist without the other.

Settling into summer

To my mind, the flower beds are now at their best, although not perhaps in the traditional gardening sense, as many of the herbaceous border perennials are not yet in flower. But I have many patches given over to flowering plants, such as marigolds, hollyhocks, foxgloves, borage and forget-me-nots, that need little or no care and can be depended upon to come up year after year. There are flowers to satisfy all sorts of pollinating insects from moths and butterflies to bees and hoverflies, in a glorious mixture of native and introduced plants. Not all are the usual occupants of a herbaceous border, some often being regarded as weeds, but all contribute cover, food and living space for insects. Honeybees busy themselves at the tall, mauve spikes of rosebay willowherb, and bumblebees zoom from hollyhock to hollyhock, landing spread-eagled on each flower and clambering up to the nectaries at its centre. Freshly opened flowers have a tight cluster of powdery cream stamens, like a lathered shaving brush, at the centre; after a day or two, the knob of stamens loosens, and the stigma pokes from their midst and expands like a diminutive pink or white chimney-sweep's brush. Valerian and buddleia are the centre of attention for butterflies; hoverflies bask and feed on tawny *Rudbeckia*, white marguerites and other flat, composite flowers. There is a wealth of blues, beloved of bees: tall, spiky teasels stand sentinel over perennial cornflower, *Veronica*, lavender and sage, and nettle-leaved bellflower adds its delicate stateliness to the scene. Creeping-Jenny extends its yellow-spangled fronds across open patches, and a jungle of wild strawberry, feverfew and wood avens shelters and shades a host of beetles, spiders, centipedes and other ground-dwellers. Clear yellow evening primroses and honeysuckle perfume the evening air, and the silvery flowers of a clump of nicotiana in the lawn bed release a cloud of scent so powerful that it forms an almost tangible belt across the garden.

Aphid numbers are really booming now, their honeydew dripping from leaves and splashing on the paths, and they are the focal point of a variety of feeding activities. Some insects eat aphids; others exploit honeydew as a rich and readily available source of sugars; hoverflies do both, at different stages of their development. A worker of *Bombus lucorum*, one of the white-tailed species, and a *Vespula* wasp are licking sugary smears on the leaves of a flowering cherry sucker. They are joined by a yellow- and black-banded hoverfly, *Syrphus ribesii*, which then moves to a cluster of aphids, where it lays an egg; this will hatch into a larva that preys on aphids. A quick search reveals flattened, opalescent hoverfly larvae – like miniature sea-slugs – amongst aphids on many plants, including cabbages, nettles, goldenrod and elder; elder aphids are black, and the gut contents show as a black streak through the transparent tissues of the hoverfly larvae that eat them.

Creeping thistle (*Cirsium arvense*), which is trying hard, despite my efforts, to colonize an area of the front garden, is also infested with aphids, amongst which prowl 2-spot ladybirds and their orange-spotted, black larvae. The larvae in particular are voracious predators of aphids, able to move astonishingly fast on their straddling black legs. They are capable of tackling much more lively prey, including each other. In June 1976, when there were ladybird eggs and newly hatched larvae all over the garden, cannibalism was rife, although the larvae were also at risk from other predators. There were several batches of eggs on the tall leaves of yellow flag, amongst which a *Tegeneria* spider had built a hammock web. As the eggs hatched, the babies fell from the leaves into the spider's web, where they become entangled, but every night the web was cleared. An active, pale brown, long-bodied spider, *Tibellus oblongus*, amongst the aphids and ladybirds on the creeping thistle, is also probably eating ladybird larvae.

Hedge bindweed has established an underground network of intertwining roots the length of one side of the garden, and its spiralling shoots climb up roses, honeysuckle, forsythia, beauty bush and Michaelmas daisies, in their upwards struggle towards the light. Its heart-shaped leaves add to the glorious jumble of foliage in the northwest corner of the garden, where it scrambles through purple-flowered mallow, tall spires of mauve bellflowers, golden buttercups, feathery fennel, prickly loganberries, and the big, rough leaves of wych elm suckers. Bindweed in moderation is an attractive addition to the garden, with its opulent flowers, but keeping it within bounds is a never-ending task. Trying to eradicate it would mean digging up a third of the garden, and even that might not work, for every fragment broken from the brittle roots seems to grow. I shall just have to go on disentangling and pulling out offending shoots, and console myself with the elegant flowers.

7

JULY

Swifts overhead

July provides a breathing space between the season of sowing and planting out, and the time of harvesting and pruning. On hot, dry days, broom pods split explosively and release their seeds, forming a staccato accompaniment to the pleasurable task of raspberry-picking. The tubular, ivory-coloured flowers of privet divert butterflies from their flight over the shrubbery, and add a curious, almost animal, scent to the garden perfumes. The *Lavatera* is a confection of flowers, sugar-pink streaked with creamy white, looking good enough to eat. There are always jobs to be done, but it is not such a busy month for the gardener, and I have more time to watch plants grow and enjoy the garden animals.

I can combine the leisurely summer job of dead-heading with keeping an eye on birds and insects. Many garden plants produce a new crop of flowers if the old ones are removed before seeds develop, and dead-heading of roses is well known as a means of prolonging the flowering season. Although the double varieties of rose are not particularly attractive to flower-visiting insects, which have difficulty reaching the nectar and pollen, I enjoy the flowers and so remove most of the dead ones. I make an exception, however, of briar roses and the floribunda 'Masquerade', because their fruits add a welcome splash of colour to the dull days of autumn. Buddleia, a powerful attractant for butterflies, marigolds, beloved by hoverflies, and perennial cornflower, visited by bees, all respond well to dead-heading, and with careful attention their flowering season can be extended by weeks or even months.

Most birds keep a low profile in July and are inconspicuous, so the entire family was alerted by a noisy avian commotion in the flowering cherry tree early one morning. Sparrows, robins, blackbirds and great tits scolded and harassed a dark shape amongst the leaves. 'A tawny owl. I can see its tail.' 'Isn't it big?' 'Why doesn't it fly away?' 'Look, it's moving up the branch!' Then a long, furry tail dropped into view, pointed ears emerged, and the inquisitive face of a ginger cat peered out of the foliage. Which shows how easily mistakes are made in identifying animals!

Many birds are still feeding fledged young, but there is ample cover for them to feed and rest unobserved. Sooner or later, when weeding or dead-heading in the herbaceous border, I am bound to disturb a young blackbird which scrabbles clumsily away while its mother scolds me. Sparrows and starlings are galvanized into unaccustomed activity by the rare event of a large dragonfly hawking for insects over the garden. A sparrow optimistically chases it, but misses; a starling is successful, and that terminates a short-lived addition to the garden's insect life. Unusual bird visitors in July – three different species of parrots – are presumably a consequence of the warm weather tempting owners of cage birds to give them an airing. Parrots are noisy and their alien sound quickly attracts attention, but there are other silent and more furtive garden visitors, only seen by the sharp-eyed, such as a chiffchaff diligently searching the apple boughs for small insects. Redpolls and their young visit the silver birch tree outside the dining-room windows, day after day, to eat the seeds, leaving the ground beneath strewn with those they have dropped. The blue berries of *Mahonia* are a focus of attention for blackbirds and song thrushes; goldfinches feast on ragwort and perennial cornflower seeds; and greenfinches work methodically over sage plants, pulling the round black seeds from the dry, bell-like calyx.

Suburban swifts

In July, swifts wheel and scream in the sky above the garden. Their elegant, black silhouettes, tracing ever-changing patterns against the clear blue of early morning or the opalescent glow of evening, lift the spirits of the most earthbound gardener. So adventurous and opportunist is the swifts' story, that they rank as buccaneers of the sky, for they visit us for only three months of the year, spending August to May far away in tropical Africa. In the nine years from 1973 to 1981, the earliest arrival over my garden was on 8 May, and the latest 16 May, and if they are not here by the second week of May, I find myself eagerly scanning the sky for the first glimpse of them. Their departure in August is as abrupt as their arrival. For several evenings there are noisy, low-level swoops between the houses by gangs of young birds – like so many black-clad youths going for a 'burn-up' on their motor-bikes – and then they have gone, usually between 8 and 16 August. Arrival and departure dates may be earlier or later in different parts of the country and in different years; in Oxford, in 1972, for instance, a healthy young bird left the nest as late as 22 September.

Why do they come? Why leave tropical skies and warmth for the cooler north? The answer lies in their feeding habits. Swifts are efficient hunters of the small flying insects and drifting spiders that constitute aerial plankton. Although available throughout the year in some parts of the tropics, aerial plankton is never as abundant and readily available as it is during the northern summer, when an entire year's insect production is telescoped into a few months. Swifts travel north in order to raise their young when they can exploit this summer flush of aerial plankton.

Swifts spend much of their time on the wing, and can neither perch nor take off from the ground. They nest in holes high above the ground, using ventilators in church towers or other tall buildings, and gaps beneath the roofs of cottages or suburban houses. In England, they are thus very much birds of town and suburbs, although on the continent they sometimes use holes in trees and cliffs. Every summer I hope that they will find a hole beneath the eaves of this house, so that I may have truly resident swifts, but they never find anything to their liking, although they nest nearby.

Each female lays two or three eggs, and there are young in the nest throughout July, which is the best month for aerial plankton. Feeding young in the nest is the hardest time of year for adult birds, as they have to collect enough food not only for themselves but also for their growing brood. Although the gape of a swift is wide, it is no easy task for them to collect enough aerial plankton, as each small food item is sighted and captured individually. They are retained in the throat until the adult has collected 300-1000 food items, which distend its neck like a goitre. On its return to the nest, it usually gives the entire squirming ball to one gaping nestling. As in other birds, there is an interval of at least 24 hours between the laying of successive eggs, and since swifts start to incubate a day before the last egg is laid, a clutch of three gives two similarly-sized and one smaller nestling. The smallest is fed less often as it competes less well for parental attention than its larger brood mates, and in some years the smallest nestlings die of starvation. This is not the loss that it may seem to be, for it increases the amount of food available to the surviving nestlings. If the weather in July is cold and wet, there is less insect activity, and swifts cannot obtain enough food for their young. They feed most quickly and efficiently when it is fine and sunny, without too much wind, and in good summers the parents can provide enough food for all their brood.

Swifts' food can be collected by gently relieving nestlings of food balls soon after they have been fed. Such collections have been made from relatively accessible colonies, and the prey items have been identified. Aphids and small flies form the bulk of their food, together with winged ants, tiny wasps, small beetles, and an unexpectedly large number of small spiders, mostly immature individuals which drift through the air on silken threads as a means of dispersal. These are the same sorts of spiders that carpet lawns and drape bushes with fine gossamer so obvious in the early morning sun when it is wet with dew. Swifts are amazingly selective feeders, distinguishing, for instance, drone honey-bees from stinging females, but the main factor determining what they catch seems to be size. Insects above a certain size are difficult to catch, hold and swallow; the smallest insects give a poor return for the amount of effort expended in their capture. The range of species taken by swifts is enormous, probably more than for any other predator. At least 65 species of aphids have been identified, many of them well-known pests of garden crops, such as the black bean aphid, and the flies include about 20 common garden species of hoverflies. This emphasizes the swifts' dependence on the abundance of aphids in temperate climates, for the common species of garden hoverflies are predators of aphids as larvae. Swifts seek out places where aerial plankton is abundant, often over gardens or agricultural land, usually feeding between two and ten metres above the ground, although they fly higher in still, fine weather and lower when it is overcast and windy.

A brood of swifts is fed about 40 times a day, which represents the individual capture of about 20,000 food items, and a pair and their brood consume nearly a million insects and spiders during July alone. This gives some idea of the density of the clouds of insects rising from suburban gardens. No wonder it is worth the swifts' while to embark on the long journey north to breed and raise their young.

The attractions of rosebay willowherb

Apart from the elegance of its flowers, rosebay willowherb is the centre of so much insect activity that it is always sure of a place in my garden, even if its invasive underground stems have to be fairly ruthlessly restricted. Apart from bees that visit the flowers, there is a whole microcosm of interactions on its leaves, especially in July; aphids suck sugary phloem sap from the leaf veins and excrete copious honeydew which hoverflies, wasps and bumblebees lap up; deceptively sluggish-looking hoverfly larvae glide through aphid clusters, occasionally seizing one, draining it dry, and discarding an empty skin; and bright 7-spot ladybirds and their larvae browse on the aphids.

At the base of rosebay willowherb stems I sometimes find an exotic-looking caterpillar, about eight centimetres long, green or dark brown, with a short 'horn' at the back and two pairs of eye-like spots near the head end. This is a caterpillar of the elegant, pink and olive-green elephant hawk moth, which was on the wing in June. By day they shelter at the base of the stem, and emerge at night, climb up the plant and munch the leaves. Rosebay willowherb is a northern plant, and its leaves are available in abundance for only a few months of the year. Elephant hawk moths have tailored their life histories and reproductive behaviour to fit the brief period of availability of food for the young, just as swifts have, although they achieve this in a different way. Rather than spending nine months of the year, like swifts, thousands of miles away, elephant hawks remain as pupae, insulated from what is happening around them. Swifts migrate, elephant hawk moths go into hiding: two solutions to the same problem.

Elephant hawk caterpillars are so much larger than the common garden caterpillars, that they seem enormous, and to add to the effect, the rather tiny head and the first two segments are retracted when not feeding, so that the region bearing the eye-spots is inflated and conspic-uous. Newly hatched elephant hawk caterpillars are green, but most turn brown after the third or fourth moult. The colour of the larger caterpillars is related to how crowded they are, and this can be investi-gated by rearing them in jam jars. Anyway, it is rather satisfactory to be in a position to tell visitors that you must just pop out and feed the elephants. In 1975, two female elephant hawks ripe with eggs were caught in the light trap; each was confined on willowherb in a bag of fine netting, and duly laid large numbers of pinhead-sized eggs. These were left to hatch and then, by dint of careful searching, the tiny green caterpillars were collected and transferred to kilner jars, either singly or in batches of five. Fresh willowherb leaves were supplied as needed, so that food shortage was not a factor affecting development. Most of the 40 caterpillars reared alone turned brown at their fourth moult (into the fifth and last caterpillar instar); three turned brown at the third moult, and four were still green when they pupated. All the crowded caterpil-lars turned brown before pupating, most of them at the third moult.

Crowded caterpillars are more active, eat more, and develop more rapidly than solitary ones, and this may affect their colour. Since caterpillars feed at night, the value of their colour for camouflage must relate to where they rest by day. Small caterpillars, all of which are green, rest beneath willowherb leaves, aligned along the midrib of the leaf. Larger caterpillars seek refuge at the base of the plant, where the background colour is predominantly the brown of soil and dead leaves, resulting in selective advantage (increased probability of surviving to reproduce) for fifth instar caterpillars being brown. A hungry bird that surprises a large caterpillar is furthermore likely to be frightened away by the eye-like markings. A single green caterpillar is not particularly conspicuous because leaf litter always includes some newly-fallen green leaves, but several large green caterpillars are more likely to attract attention. This may be the evolutionary reason why all crowded elephant hawk moth caterpillars are brown in the fifth instar, and also why many turn brown earlier than solitary caterpillars.

Protective coloration
Animals such as moths that rest motionless by day are continually at risk from predators that hunt by sight. Indeed, few animals are safe from predators; most have evolved strategies for avoiding being eaten, and these usually involve some sort of protective coloration. Colour and pattern can serve as protection in many different ways: as camouflage, deception, or distraction, to startle a predator, or to warn it not to touch. Predators too may be camouflaged, to reduce the risks of being seen by their prey.

Moths that rest by day in exposed positions on tree trunks are not only camouflaged so that they match their background, but are also adept at selecting the most appropriate background and orienting themselves so that camouflage is perfected. Brown bars on the wings of the brindled beauty, for instance, merge with the pattern of striations on bark. The mottling of a peppered moth blends inconspicuously with the variegated rough surface of lichens. The small blood-vein settles with the wings partly spread, so that a dark, red-brown stripe on each hind wing is continuous with similar stripes on the fore wings. Out of context, this is conspicuous, but when it orients itself on a tree trunk with its body parallel with the ground, the red stripe is just another crack in the bark. Moths that sit on tree trunks rest with the wings pressed close and flat against the surface so that they seem almost two-dimensional, with no shadow. The garden carpet uses an additional strategy; it lands on a tree trunk or fence head up, then quickly turns upside-down before settling, a movement guaranteed to confuse a watching predator. Just as effective a camouflage as matching the background is obliteration of outline, so that a moth does not look moth-shaped. The flame shoulder and the setaceous Hebrew character have conspicuous pale marks at the leading edge of their brownish fore wings; at rest, they are held close together covering the hind wings, bringing the pale marks to the sides so that the outline is disrupted, and the apparent shape is nothing like a moth. Camouflage depends on absolute stillness if it is to be effective. Camouflaged moths freeze quickly when they alight, so that they apparently disappear from view, and they are unresponsive when prodded.

From the mid-nineteenth century onwards, tree trunks in cities and industrial areas in Britain and western Europe became increasingly blackened with soot and lost their covering of lichens, which are intolerant of pollution. A moth adapted to blend visually with bark or lichens is conspicuous on a blackened tree trunk, and becomes an obvious and easy target for a hungry bird. When industrial pollution began to spread, black (or melanic) mutants of a number of species of moths common in urban areas began to increase in numbers relative to the usual pale forms. Melanics are inconspicuous on polluted tree trunks and, since melanism is inherited, their increase in relative frequency is a consequence of their improved chances of survival to reproduce. By the 1960s, the vast majority of individuals of the peppered moth (*Biston betularia*) in cities and downwind of industrial areas were black. In country areas, however, where tree trunks still retained their lichens, the pale form remained the commonest. There is no evidence that pollution caused melanism in moths, only that it led to rapid spread of an advantageous characteristic. The advantage is enhanced because moths seem to select the background that they best match. There is however some evidence that the caterpillars of the black forms are less sensitive than those of pale forms to chemical pollutants that they ingest along with their food.

The peppered moth is not particularly common in my garden, although some are caught every year in the light trap. They are elegant, shapely moths, and the way that they rest on the trap sides, with the spread wings flush with the surface and the antennae depressed, shows clearly how their behaviour is adapted to perfect their match to the background. Almost all the peppered moths caught in the trap before 1978 were melanics, but recently there has been a small increase in the frequency of the pale form, almost certainly because 'clean air' policies and the declaration of smokeless zones have led to re-establishment of lichens on tree trunks. The dark form is so conspicuous on a lichen-covered tree trunk, and the pale form on a polluted surface, that the selective advantage in matching the background is very strong, leading to rapid change in the character of the population. This is evolution in action, and moths prove to be sensitive indicators of environmental change in urban areas.

Many insects resemble the leaves or twigs amongst which they rest: the comma butterfly hangs from a branch with only the dark underside of the jagged wings showing, exactly like a dead leaf or piece of torn bark, and many moths, including the poplar hawk and angle shades, look like dead brown leaves. The buff-tip moth has conspicuous pale tips to its greyish wings, but when at rest on a dead twig, with its wings folded together, it looks like a broken side shoot. Stick caterpillars, such as those of the peppered moth, are effectively camouflaged, like either green or brown twigs, down to the marks and scars that twigs bear. Even the bright brimstone butterfly looks like a leaf as it hangs from a branch in winter; the reddish-brown marks on the underside of its wings look like blemishes or spots of fungus. Some moths look like chips of wood, and others escape detection by resembling bird droppings. As with camouflage, stillness is essential to the deception. I heard convincing proof of the efficacy of the Chinese character's protective coloration from someone who runs a light trap at his house on Romney Marsh. Every morning, by the time he inspects the catch, sparrows have eaten any moths that settled nearby, leaving the surrounding area liberally daubed with their droppings. One morning, he realized that the sparrows had missed one moth, for resting immobile amongst their droppings was a Chinese character.

Moths that are inactive by day, provide many examples of camouflage and deception. Butterflies, on the other hand, are active by day, but many gain some protection from birds, by distracting a predator's attention from their vulnerable heads and bodies. White lines on the underside of the hind wings of the white-letter hairstreak converge on a row of black-centred orange spots and a short 'tail' at the wing edge; when it alights and closes the wings, these markings at the back are more conspicuous than its head. The most striking elements in a butterfly's pattern are nearly always at the edges of the wings, and many have contrasting markings at the wing tips, i.e. at the farthest point from the body. The high frequency of butterflies with beak marks at the edges and tips of their wings is proof that these conspicuous patterns serve to divert a predator's strike from the more vulnerable areas.

Other protective uses of colour depend on sudden movement, such as the way in which an eyed hawk moth exposes its large false eyes when disturbed. A small bird, foraging along a branch, might well be fooled by the camouflage of the moth's fore wings and inadvertently peck at it; it would then get the fright of its life when confronted with a pair of eyes, half a centimetre in diameter, and two-and-a-half centimetres apart! The intimidating effect is enhanced by the moth rocking back and forth, so that the enormous eyes seem to move threateningly. Many moths, butterflies and caterpillars use an exaggerated false face of one sort or another as threat, the essential element being prominent eyes. Sometimes it is exposed suddenly, but often it is more or less permanently on show, like a peacock butterfly's eye-markings, or those on fully-grown caterpillars of elephant hawk moths. If it cannot escape, a peacock butterfly under threat orients its eye-markings towards the attacker, and makes a soft hissing noise by rubbing its wings together; an elephant hawk caterpillar bunches up the front end of its body, so that the eye-markings become more conspicuous. In most cases, such behaviour is pure bluff, but occasionally there is some back-up to the threat, as when a menacing puss moth caterpillar, with its writhing red 'tails', regurgitates acrid-smelling food remains.

Palatable insects have a number of options open to them, in the evolutionary sense: they can avoid being eaten by flight, by hiding, by camouflage of one sort or another, by looking like something else, or by bluff. Some moths, such as the large yellow underwing, have more than one defensive strategy. They rest showing only the camouflaged brown fore wings, and tend to scuttle away when gently prodded; if really disturbed, however, they fly rapidly away, exposing the brilliant yellow hind wings, then suddenly alight and 'disappear' as the fore wings cover the hind wings. In contrast, the uniformly brown mouse moth always scuttles along the ground when disturbed, which is how it earned its name. Whatever a moth's strategy, there is selective advantage in doing it well. Individuals that flee most rapidly, hide most completely, best match their background, most closely resemble a stick or bird dropping, or most convincingly frighten a predator, are more likely to survive to reproduce and perpetuate their coloration than those that do it less well. In every generation, poor performers are weeded out, and so the strategies are perfected. There is another option open to palatable insects, and that is to masquerade as poisonous or distasteful insects.

Some colours that are always on show are a definite warning not to touch. The bold yellow and black of a wasp and the striking chocolate-brown, white and scarlet of a garden tiger moth are labels that advertise poisonous properties. It is a fairly safe assumption that insects that flaunt brilliant colours and patterns are dangerous or at least distasteful to predators, whereas insects that use colour to avoid detection, or to startle predators, tend to be palatable. Tasty insects that mimic those that are nasty to eat, often do so with amazing accuracy. Clearwing moths, for instance, are mimics of wasps, and anyone would think twice about touching a hornet clearwing, so close is the resemblance. Many flies mimic bees or wasps. Different colour forms of the hoverfly known as the narcissus fly resemble different species of bumblebees, and drone flies (also hoverflies) are very like honeybees; like other bee mimics, they tend to hang about on flowers, adding to the similarity. More often, however, resemblance is generalized, in that flies or other insects adopt the type of colour pattern usually associated with a sting, such as yellow and black bands. Many common garden hoverflies are banded or spotted with yellow on a black abdomen: none can be matched with a particular species of wasp, yet it is reasonable to assume that all gain some protection from their colour patterns.

To understand why this should be so, we have first to consider why so many wasps are black and yellow. The more generally one particular colour pattern is associated with unpleasantness, the more quickly predators that hunt by sight learn to leave it alone. Individuals that fit in with a universal colour-coding stand the best chance of surviving to reproduce, thus contributing their colour pattern to the next generation. The mavericks, however, striking their colours, are more likely to be attacked by predators that fail to recognize them, and so are less likely to reproduce. Natural selection leads to the adoption and retention of the same label by many different sorts of unpalatable insects. It is rather like the way we standardize the labelling of poisonous chemicals, radioactive materials or dangerous electrical installations: the significance of a skull and cross-bones is generally understood, whatever language people use.

There must be enormous selective advantage for a palatable insect in breaking into the system of colour-coding that indicates poison. It may not be necessary to mimic one particular species, but sufficient to adopt a generalized label that means 'not for eating'. True, black and yellow hoverflies are eaten by birds and other predators, but they are able to bask quite openly on leaves and fences in the sun, apparently protected

PLATE 7   12 Orange-tip butterflies increasingly use *Arabis caucasica* as a larval foodplant (see p. 80). 13 Ragwort has escaped my weeding activities and brightens the otherwise bare yard (see p. 126). 14 Silver birch droops over hogweed, whose flat, white flower clusters attract hoverflies and other short-tongued insects, and Egyptian onions.

by the warning implicit in their colour pattern. Protection only holds good, however, for as long as the majority of insects carrying a particular colour-coding are entitled to it because they really are poisonous. Individual predators learn by experience what to eat and what to leave alone, and if a bird's first encounters with black and yellow insects are with mimics, then it will learn to eat black and yellow insects. Only if models outnumber mimics, so that a novice predator encounters more distasteful than palatable insects bearing a particular colour code, will it learn to avoid insects with that label.

Tapping plant sugars

By mid-July, my silver birches support vast numbers of large aphids. They spatter the grass, paths and plants beneath, as well as most of the birch leaves, with sticky honeydew, which nourishes a smothering and unsightly, black mould. Why do aphids do this? The answer lies in their method of feeding. An aphid has piercing mouthparts which are inserted into the phloem tissue of a plant. Phloem consists largely of tube-like cells that transport manufactured sugars from the leaves to other parts of a plant. Aphids use as an energy source some of the sugars they suck in, but they also need amino acids, the building blocks for manufacturing proteins. Amino acids are present in phloem sap, but only in very low concentrations. In order to acquire sufficient amino acids for protein synthesis, aphids have to take in vast quantities of phloem sap, and they excrete the excess sugars in copious quantities as honeydew. In other words, one way in which aphids are able to exploit an unpromising food source, is by maintaining a rapid throughput of the sugars for which they have only limited use. It is parallel to the feeding strategy of spittlebugs, but honeydew is far more conspicuous than excreted water.

This is not the only strategy of aphids for acquiring sufficient nitrogenous compounds. Many species improve their food supply by alternating between two different sorts of foodplants during the course of the year. Bird cherry-oat aphids, for instance, over-winter on bird cherry as fertilized eggs. In spring, these hatch into an all-female generation that feeds on rapidly growing new leaves, which have a high nitrogen content. These aphids give rise to a succession of all-female generations produced parthenogenetically (without fertilization by a male). Aphids produced by parthenogenesis are born alive as miniatures of the parent; if a fat female aphid is carefully squashed, daughter aphids are extruded, and these, if squashed with even greater care, prove to

PLATE 8   15 Gardens are like vastly extended woodland edge, where the shelter and shade of trees gives way to sunny, open spaces (see p. 201).

contain tiny grand-daughters. As leaves mature, their nitrogen content declines, and in mid-summer, bird cherry-oat aphids move onto grasses whose leaves are still growing and so are still nutritious. In the autumn, when grasses die back, the aphids return to bird cherry, the nitrogen content of whose leaves again increases as they become senescent. Eventually a generation of males and females is produced, mate, and lay fertilized eggs which over-winter to repeat the cycle.

Switching foodplants, when aphid numbers have increased to such a level that they are conspicuous, is probably also a way of avoiding predators and parasites. Black bean aphids (*Aphis fabae*) lay eggs in autumn on spindle, mock orange and various species of *Viburnum*. The following spring the eggs hatch into wingless females, which give rise to vast numbers of daughters parthenogenetically, and by June my mock orange is dripping with honeydew. The next generation are winged females, and these fly off to produce several more generations parthenogenetically on beans, spinach, thistles and many herbaceous plants. Not until autumn are winged males produced, and these and females return to spindle, mock orange and *Viburnum*. The females give birth to another generation of wingless females, which mate with the males, and lay over-wintering eggs.

Other sorts of aphids are gall-makers, and this too is related to improving the quality of their food. The spiral galls that appeared on the leaf stalks, or petioles, of poplar in May are caused by the aphid, *Pemphigus spirothecae*. An over-wintered female makes a series of punctures with her feeding stylets in a zigzag pattern across a petiole. Growth is inhibited in the band of cells that she punctures, but proceeds normally on the opposite side of the petiole, so that as it grows it bends to form a loose spiral. Further punctures stimulate each coil to grow sideways into adjacent coils, until the female is enclosed by the twisted, enlarged petiole within which she and her progeny feed. Changes in the plant's metabolism induced by some component in the aphid's saliva, improve the quality of the tissue as a food source. Large leaves are at a premium when over-wintered females are seeking petioles on which to establish themselves, for the larger the leaf, the more offspring a female produces, and the quicker they develop.

The quality of aphids' food is also enhanced by their association with plant viruses, because the sap of infected plants contains more amino acids. Viruses are transmitted from plant to plant by the feeding activities of aphids; some sorts of viruses are merely transported passively on the feeding stylets, but others enter the aphid's circulation and after several hours reach the salivary glands so that virus is injected with saliva when the aphid feeds. Aphids are thus vectors of plant viruses in the same way that mosquitoes are vectors of human blood parasites. They suffer no ill effects either from virus infection or from feeding on infected plants. Indeed their food supply is improved, so that the benefits to virus and aphid are mutual.

Aphids are effectively sedentary; they do not have to be hunted and captured by predators, but can be browsed. Since they reproduce asexually, their relationship with their predators is more like that of a plant with herbivores than that of prey with hunters. Hoverfly larvae, lacewing larvae, and adult and larval ladybirds browse aphids, achieving incredible consumption. Usually rain soon washes honeydew from birch leaves, but in dry summers it persists as a gummy coating which hinders the movement of larval ladybirds, and they crowd onto clean leaves that have been protected from the sugary shower by other leaves. In years when birch aphids do well, so do ladybirds. Not that an aphid is totally compliant when grabbed by a hungry ladybird; it kicks, it extrudes globules of sticky wax from a pair of tubular glands near its rear end, and it may disengage its feeding stylets and walk away, or if all else fails, drop from the plant. Moreover, aphids tend to feed head downwards, so that they are facing the direction from which a predator is likely to approach, and they react to the aroma of glandular secretion released by one of their number by taking evasive action.

The most ubiquitous and ferocious predators of small insects are undoubtedly ants, but aphids have come to terms with ants in a curious way. Ants avidly consume sugary fluids and, far from attacking aphids, some species solicit honeydew production by tapping and stroking them with their antennae; they move aphids to the most productive part of a plant, and in the case of root-feeding aphids, move them into their underground nests and care for them and their progeny like their own brood. It is much more than a casual relationship: many aphids associated with ants are never found unattended, and, moreover, only produce honeydew when solicited; instead of a long posterior process for ejecting honeydew, attended aphids have a circlet of hairs around the anus, to retain honeydew; and, since their ant attendants are an effective defence, they lack wax-producing glands. The closeness of the bond varies, some species of ants tending many species of aphids, others being associated with just one, but all such relationships are mutually beneficial and adaptive; the aphids are sheltered, protected and assured of food, and the ants have a limitless supply of sugar on tap.

Aphids and the gardener

We tend to assume, especially as gardeners, that aphids are harmful to plants, because they extract nutrients. Certainly heavily infested plants produce less healthy green foliage and appear stunted. In boom years for birch aphids, the trees respond by shedding their leaves prematurely, and by the end of July my garden is littered with yellow leaves. But a plant is adapted only to ensure production of seeds that constitute the next generation, and as long as this is possible, abundance and persistence of foliage are irrelevant. The substance most often in short supply to plants is nitrogen, which they absorb in solution as nitrates through their roots. A major source of soil nitrates is the activities of nitrogen-fixing bacteria, which are able to convert atmospheric nitrogen to nitrates. There is some evidence that the addition of sugar to soil increases the rate of nitrogen fixation, and hence the total quantity of nitrates formed over a period of time. Much of the sugar removed from phloem by aphids falls onto the soil beneath the plant as honeydew. A 14-metre lime tree may support over a million aphids, which scatter about 400 grams of sugar beneath the tree every day. There may be over 5,000 million aphids per hectare of vegetation, so that collectively they saturate the soil with sugar. If, as seems likely, this results in increased availability of nitrates to plants, then plants are using aphids to divert sugars manufactured during photosynthesis into the soil, where they lead to improved nitrate supplies. As yet, these interactions between plants, aphids and bacteria are not fully understood, but we should certainly hesitate before branding aphids as an unmitigated nuisance.

As a consequence of their specialized feeding method, most species of aphid are restricted to a few foodplants, often just the two between which they alternate. Consequently there may be nearly as many species of aphid in a garden as there are cultivated plants, and even those that look alike may not be the same species. A traditional tip for ridding beans of 'blackfly' is to stick leafy elder twigs in the ground close to the bean plants, on the assumption that the aphids will move onto the elder. But, despite appearances, the black aphid that clusters thickly on green elder stems in summer is a different species.

The phenomenal rate of increase in numbers of aphids on beans, roses, or any other garden plant in summer is largely a consequence of the rapid succession of parthenogenetic generations. The problem they pose to the gardener has no easy solution, because it is almost impossible to kill an aphid. That may sound like a nonsense statement, but think of how all those summer generations are produced. They are little more than buds produced vegetatively. In other words, the aphids infesting a bean plant are all genetically identical, differing from each other no more than the leaves of.the bean plant. Kill a few hundred and all you have done is to prune a super-aphid, and as long as one aphid is left, the genetic individual survives and grows to give more aphids. Estimates of the size of aphid populations are almost impossible to obtain, because the aphids you can see and count are not genetic individuals, but only 'bits'. As long as a few survive, the genetic individual persists to over-winter, and next year grows and buds again, to produce another enormous, though fragmented, super-aphid.

Pathway to summer

There is such a luxuriance of informal growth in my garden, that by mid-summer it has become a continual exercise to push back and curb the exuberant vegetation that threatens to obliterate even the paths. I find that weeding and tidying paths is a splendid rationale for sitting outside while feeling that I am doing something useful. Path policy is, however, very personal, even idiosyncratic. I have given up arguing with those who think I do it wrong, whether other members of my family, or well-intentioned passers-by who pause at the gate to proffer unsolicited advice. One gentleman, I recall, advised me to pour petrol in all the gaps between the paving stones to suppress weed growth – surely a profligate and messy solution! I see no hopes of resolving the argument as to whether path stones are disturbed more by root growth of weeds or the action of pulling them out, since both must have an effect.

I should explain that the main paths in the back garden are York stone slabs, warm to the eye and touch in sunshine, although decidedly slippery when wet. A space for cars at the front, the side yard, and an area behind the house are covered with more mundane paving stones, and smaller paths are covered with motley crazy paving. I like many of the small plants that green the spaces in the paths – pearlwort, hairy bitter-cress, liverworts and mosses, the purple-leaved yellow oxalis, wild thyme, forget-me-nots, thyme-leaved speedwell, and stonecrops – but fight a continuing battle with creeping buttercup, marguerite daisies, Canadian fleabane, pink oxalis, and various grasses. I suppose in a warm summer I spend a total of several days on my knees or sitting on the warm slabs, investigating the growth in the cracks. Investigating, because I refuse to clear the gaps, or indeed do any weeding, indiscriminately. Nothing is pulled out until I know what it is. This means that baffling new-comers are left until they flower, by which time they may be so much a part of the garden scene that they are left undisturbed. Larger plants may be spared my weeding knife if they add a welcome patch of colour to a bare corner: the occasional ragwort or feverfew plant is reprieved on this basis, especially in the yard, where they brighten the otherwise dull view from the kitchen sink; and I can rarely bring myself to pull out buddleia seedlings, sage or wallflowers, unless they are really in the way. Despite this, I find neat, swept paths eminently satisfying, and feel that their smooth order is the perfect foil for the profusion of unregimented growth encouraged around them. My obsession with paths has its rewards – a number of plants on the garden list were first discovered during these nose-to-ground weeding forays – and there is much to see, for there is continual activity in the cracks between the paving stones, particularly on the part of ants.

Ants are social insects, and, as in bees and wasps, a colony consists for most of the year of an egg-laying queen and non-breeding females, or workers, which are her offspring. Worker ants are wingless, but they forage for food, maintain the nest, tend the queen, and care for her enormous brood. Eventually, however, the queen lays eggs which develop into winged males and females capable of mating, laying eggs and founding new colonies. The reproductives that emerge from a single nest are brothers and sisters, and genetically very similar, but the chances of outbreeding with males and females from different nests are increased by synchronous emergence of swarms of winged ants from many nests of the same species. Synchrony of mating flights is only achieved because ants of the same species respond similarly to a given set of weather and atmospheric conditions – for the garden black ant, *Lasius niger*, warm, thundery weather in July. There is strong selection for all colonies to respond to the same factor, because those that are out of phase make a smaller contribution, if any, to the next generation.

Swarms of winged ants cause quite a commotion. As I glance up from my weeding, I am puzzled to see large numbers of black-headed gulls, circling and dipping in the air above the garden. The nearest sea is the Wash, nearly 150 kilometres away, and a hundred years ago, black-headed gulls in Leicestershire were considered as accidental stragglers. Nowadays, however, vast flocks roost at local reservoirs in winter and feed throughout the city; increasingly they are a feature of the summer fauna as well, and a few pairs have bred in the county. The gulls above the garden are evidently feeding, hawking for something present in the air in large numbers. Close inspection of the ground beneath explains the gulls' interest. In half a dozen places in the garden, mostly on steps or paths, tiny wingless ants marshal a jostling crowd of larger, winged ants emerging from a newly excavated hole surrounded by fine granules of soil. One after another, followed by more and more, they take off and rise into the air. Sparrows and starlings, ever watchful for something to eat, quickly take advantage of this bonanza, and successfully, if rather clumsily, catch a few before they get very far. Agile house martins dart across the garden and snatch rather more, but most, caught in thermal up-draughts, rise many metres into the air to where the hungry gulls circle.

8

AUGUST

Buddleia is beautiful

If I were to nominate flowers that epitomize different months of the year, for August I should choose *Buddleia davidii*. I have bushes all over the garden; they are pruned hard in the winter, grow vigorously each spring into dense, arching masses of vegetation, and by August are covered with long, drooping sprays of purple flowers. Buddleia does well in urban areas, as witnessed by the way it runs colourful riot on derelict or neglected city sites. It quickly establishes itself on building rubble and successfully shades out other invaders, not because it needs chalky soil, but rather because it is tolerant of it, and competes for space particularly successfully with other colonizers. It may also be that the downy hairs on the underside of the leaves to some extent shield from pollution the pores through which gas exchange takes place. It is prolific, ubiquitous and beautiful, with the bonus of being a good insect plant.

Buddleia flowers act like a magnet to butterflies, and on a sunny day are crowded with small tortoiseshells, peacocks, red admirals, green-veined whites, and both large and small cabbage whites. There is always a chance of seeing a small copper, or a rare garden visitor, like the silver-washed fritillary that I surprised on buddleia in the drought year, and, if painted ladies are around, that is where they too will be found. Individual flowers are small, but, to judge by the avidity with which butterflies feed at them, are rich in nectar, and feeding opportunities are improved by the way flowers are massed together into sprays. Their scent is fruity in character, which is thought to be why they are particularly attractive to red admirals and other butterflies that feed on the juices of fallen fruit. Individual flower tubes are about seven millimetres long, so the nectar is too deep for short-tongued bees and for most flower-feeding flies, although readily accessible to butterflies and moths. Regular visitors also include bumblebees and long-tongued hoverflies, such as the drone fly and other species of *Eristalis*, strikingly patterned, yellow and black *Helophilus*, and *Rhingia campestris*, with its curious protruding snout.

It is not just buddleia that is busy, for hoverflies, butterflies, and, indeed, garden insects in general reach their peak abundance and variety in August. The pale flowers of mint prove a great attraction to bees, flies and beetles of all sizes, and the hanging, blue, star-like flowers of borage dip and sway with the weight of feeding bumblebees. Everywhere I look, on white marguerites, on pink stonecrop, on yellow ragwort, and on feathery sprays of goldenrod, there are hoverflies, and the lawn bed, warmed by the morning sun, is alive with them. Their wings make an iridescent blur as they dart to and fro, hovering motionless then apparently vanishing, only to reappear a couple of metres away. Three medium-sized black and yellow species dominate the scene: broadly-banded *Syrphus ribesii*, intricately-banded *Episyrphus balteatus*, and *Metasyrphus corollae* marked with pairs of pale lunules. Some feed at russet *Rudbeckia*, brilliant orange pot marigolds, acid yellow African marigolds, tawny and golden French marigolds, and royal blue dwarf convolvulus; others bask on large runner bean leaves or hoary cabbages; and egg-laying females inspect clusters of aphids. An *E.balteatus* is unconcernedly vandalizing an evening primrose, by eating pollen from the stigma – a sophisticated piece of thieving!

Summer drought

1975 and 1976 are remembered as 'good summers'. In other words, there were prolonged periods of hot, dry weather, and there was no need to travel abroad for a sun-tan. 1975 was warm, but not excessively so; June and early July were dry, and the garden temporarily showed symptoms of drought, but this presented no serious problems. In 1976, however, conditions were more extreme. During a heat-wave in June and early July, temperatures in excess of 30°C were commonplace, and there was little rain. After mid-July it became somewhat cooler, but skies were clear, and there was no biologically effective rainfall until well into September, when we embarked on an unusually wet autumn. 1976 was the year of drought, when gardens withered, the countryside became parched and brown so that cattle had to be supplied with 'winter' feed in August, water supplies were rationed, and the Minister of Sport became the Minister of Drought. Waste water became too valuable to empty down the drain, and I used it to keep the soil of the lawn bed and around selected plants moist. Washing-up and laundry water were saved in a

plastic dustbin, and a hose was kept permanently hoisted to the bath-
room window so that bath water could be siphoned onto the garden –
simple in theory, though not in practice!

As long as adequate soil water is accessible to their roots, plants do
well in summers like that of 1975, when growth was vigorous, and
flowering and fruiting prolific. The drought conditions of 1976, however, had a markedly different effect. The response of many plants to lack
of water was to flower and fruit quickly, often while still quite small. In
other words, available nutrients were diverted as soon as possible into
seeds constituting the next generation, rather than into additional
foliage. Birch trees shed their leaves early, but since they had already set
seed, this was sound economy and a way of conserving water. One horse
chestnut that I know of lost many of its leaves in mid-summer, and the
bare branches flowered in November, as though the tree's biological
clock had been set forward by several months. There was a bumper crop
of nuts and fruits, and hedgerows were scarlet with hawthorn berries,
but plants tended to channel a minimum of resources into the flesh of
fruit, which feeds the animals that disperse the seed, not the seed or
embryo plant. The effects of this were most marked in cultivated fruits,
artificially selected to be large and succulent; raspberries and loganberries seemed to be all pips, and, although my Worcester Pearmain tree
was loaded with apples, they were small and rather dry. Concentration
of available resources into production of the next generation makes good
sense as a survival strategy. Birches, chestnuts and apples quickly
recovered and got back to normal, but elms suffered a severe set-back in
1976. Many succumbed to Dutch elm disease, partly because hot, dry
conditions favour bark beetles, which carry the fungus from tree to tree,
and partly because drought, by placing extra stress on trees, lowered
their resistance.

The most immediate effects of summer drought, especially notice-
able to gardeners, are on plants, but it also influences the abundance,
seasonality and behaviour of insects. As long as it is not too hot or too dry
for prolonged periods, warm, dry weather leads to increased numbers of
insects; conditions are optimal for moving and feeding, and individual
insects grow and develop quickly. At the same time there is a tendency
for ranges to extend, and mass movements may cause sudden local
increases in numbers.

The year of the hoverflies

In the first week of August 1975 there were hoverflies everywhere: basking and hovering in the sun; feeding at every available flower, including those, such as rosebay willowherb, that they usually ignore because the nectar is not readily accessible; swarming over aphid-infested plants, licking up honeydew and laying eggs; feeding in unusual ways, such as the *E.balteatus* I saw licking exudations from hollyhock petals punctured by minute black beetles; flying in open windows to become trapped in houses; confusing picnics by getting in the sandwiches and falling in the drinks; and at night, entering the light trap in large numbers. They even made the national press, with newspaper reports of holiday-makers being driven from east coast beaches by swarms of hoverflies. Panic on the beaches, however, may have been a case of mistaken identity, as the hoverflies were predominantly the superficially wasp-like *S.ribesii, M.corollae* and *E.balteatus.*

Sudden increase in the size of Malaise trap catches demonstrated a large influx of hoverflies to the garden in the first two weeks of August. The hoverfly catch for the week ending 27 July was an unexceptional 139 of 20 different species, but the following week, 562 individuals, of 28 species, were caught, 162 of them on one day. The total for the week ending 10 August was 2,812 individuals of 33 species, and 1,557 were caught in the following week, but the catch for the week ending 24 August was down to 91. The peak days were the 7th, 8th and 12th of August, when 672, 954 and 636 individuals, respectively, were trapped, giving some idea of the vast numbers in the garden as a whole. The dominant species in the catch was *M.corollae*, 2,580 being trapped in 1975, more than the annual total of all species for some years, and there were also many *E.balteatus, S.ribesii,* and other species with aphid-feeding larvae.

Ladybirds also moved into gardens in 1975, particulary the 7-spot, which is a species of agricultural land, and the black-spotted, red 11-spot, a salt-marsh species. The feature common to ladybirds and the species of hoverflies involved, is feeding on aphids. The most likely explanation for these mass movements is that aphid numbers had boomed in the countryside and on agricultural land, as they had in gardens, in the warm, dry weather of June and July. This led to population explosions of their predators, which were then forced to move, either by depletion of their food supply or by some disturbance such as crop harvesting. Clouds of hoverflies and ladybirds drifted around the country in search of food, tending to move eastwards with the prevailing wind. Many reached the coast, where they accumulated; others settled in gardens, where many stayed. This meant that numbers remained high as a result of over-wintering and breeding, although there was a further influx of *M.corollae* and *E.balteatus*, presumably for similar reasons, in 1976. Thereafter, catches of *M.corollae* declined, year by year; only 66 were caught in 1980 and 72 in 1981. There was, however, a sudden upsurge of *E.balteatus* in 1977, when it formed nearly half the total catch. The reasons for the *E.balteatus* boom in 1977 are far from clear: it is a migratory species, and there were many reports of apparent migrations on the south coast of England, although a lively, and unresolved, controversy developed in the correspondence columns of *The Times* as to whether they were arriving or leaving!

My overall conclusion from watching and catching insects in 1975 is that warm, dry weather is associated with increased abundance, whether or not immigration is involved. Resident hoverflies and 2-spot ladybirds, did well in the garden, and the unselective Malaise trap catch confirms the impression derived from hand-netting of high butterfly numbers. Silver Y moths were common, and the Malaise trap catch of resident yellow underwings was nearly twice as high as in any other year. One of the delights of 1975 was to listen to crickets chirruping on warm, fragrant summer evenings, an unaccustomed sound in a Midland garden.

With the abundance of nectar-feeding insects, sweet fluids of any sort were at a premium in the summer of 1975, and traps baited with fermenting fruit were particularly effective. The simplest design consists of a cylinder of netting fabric, about 30 centimetres in diameter and 60 centimetres in height, closed with netting at the top, and supported top and bottom by circles of stiff wire, below which is suspended a circular board of equal diameter. The trap is hung from a branch by a handle attached to the top, and rotting fruit, or any other bait, is placed on the board. The gap between board and trap is about three centimetres, sufficient to admit butterflies, but not obvious as an exit. Insects crawl beneath the netting to feed at the bait, but when leaving tend to fly upwards where they are trapped by the closed end of the cylinder. When the trap is in operation, the weight of the board holds the netting taut, but when it is lifted down, it collapses, and captured insects can be removed for identification. The only drawback is that rotting fruit attracts large numbers of wasps. I soon learned not to leave baited traps unattended for long, as captured wasps wreak havoc in the confined space, catching and chewing the other insects. They also make removal of moths, butterflies or hoverflies somewhat hazardous! In 1975, fruit

BAITED TRAP

proved a most attractive bait, bringing in peacock butterflies, red admirals, silver Y moths, yellow underwings, a variety of other sorts of moths, and many hoverflies. These included not only abundant migrants, such as *M.corollae*, *E.balteatus* and *S.ribesii*, but also less usual species, such as *Ferdinandea cuprea*, a brassy-tinted woodland species that I have only recorded in the garden on two other occasions, and *Scaeva selenitica*, a beautiful big hoverfly, with pairs of pale lunules on its shiny, black, somewhat flattened abdomen, which is generally uncommon.

The year of the ladybirds
Both adult and larval ladybirds are predators of aphids, and so they were presumably more sensitive than hoverflies to the changes in availability

of aphids brought about by the drought of 1976. Many of the 7-spot and 11-spot ladybirds that had entered the garden the previous year, over-wintered and bred, but there were further large influxes of these and of black and yellow, checkered 14-spots, a woodland species, especially in July 1976, when the countryside was beginning to dry out and aphid numbers to crash. Like hoverflies the year before, displaced ladybirds continued moving, especially east and southwards, until they reached the beaches, where they accumulated, causing even greater drama than the hoverfly 'plagues'. They need a fluid intake, and in dry conditions tend to alight on moist surfaces to drink. Not unreasonably, they settled on the exposed bodies of perspiring sunbathers. Their drinking move-ments cause only slight tickling, but when brushed away they give the standard ladybird response to interference, which is to exude caustic fluid from their leg joints. This causes irritation to sensitive (or sun-burnt) skin, and led to the repeated, indignant charge that the ladybirds were biting.

So-called plagues are a spectacular manifestation of insect movement induced by drought and reduced food availability. Equally exciting is the appearance of insects far from their usual haunts, and increased numbers of migratory species. Butterfly numbers in 1976 were down on 1975 (as shown by Malaise trap catches), but variety was unusually great, and 19 of the 21 species known from the garden were hand-netted. The single individuals of white-letter hairstreak, hedge brown, silver-washed fritillary and marbled white netted in 1976 are the only garden records of these species. All four are countryside butterflies, and none is normally associated with towns and gardens. Drought conditions evidently forced them to move in search of nectar supplies, which they found in gardens. The explanation must be the same for the only garden records of hoverflies usually associated with woodland, such as *Criorhi-na berberina*, a hairy, rotund, black and yellow fly, and of three different species of wasp-like clearwing moths. Hot, dry conditions that keep insects on the move after nectar and other sugary fluids, tend to accentuate the travels of migratory species, so that they arrive in greater numbers than usual, or appear in areas they rarely visit. In both these respects, 1976 was a good year for migrants. Numbers of painted lady and red admiral butterflies were high, so that on some days they jostled for position on buddleia flowers, and it is the only year that I have seen hummingbird hawk moths in the garden. There were plenty of other local records of unusual visitors, such as white-letter hairstreak and marsh fritillary butterflies, and of migrants, including clouded yellow butterflies, hummingbird hawk moths and the spectacular death's-head hawk moth.

The way in which the extreme conditions of 1976 affected the seasonality of plants was paralleled in their effect on insects. Hoverflies, for instance, normally reach a peak of abundance and variety in August, but in 1976 numbers of individuals and species were well up in May and June, reached a maximum in July, and then declined rather rapidly, so that scarcely any were caught in September. The story was similar for other groups of insects: growth and production of the next generation were accelerated, and the usual seven-month season was compressed into four or five months. As the drought dragged on into late August, peacock and small tortoiseshell butterflies went into hibernation, and clusters of 7-spot ladybirds could be found huddling together beneath leaves, conserving energy and moisture. By mid-September, gardens and countryside were as still and brown as in winter, and the autumn rains came too late to alter the situation. But in 1977, after a rather slow start, seasonality was back to normal, showing the resilience of our flora and fauna.

Where have all the butterflies gone?

I often hear nostalgic laments for the myriad butterflies that once enlivened gardens in summer, and concern at their disappearance. But has the situation really changed? As a group, butterflies are abundant and diverse at low latitudes, but in the British Isles are near the northern limit of their geographical range. We tend to judge abundance by how often we see the more colourful species, but many of these are migrants from further south, which tend to move north in greater numbers in hot, dry summers. Under the same conditions, species that are local in distribution increase in numbers and then spill over into other areas in search of nectar. The further back we delve into our memories, the greater the tendency to recollect only fine summers, which are usually good for butterflies. But good summers are not all that frequent and so we tend to assume that butterflies are on the decline. Predictably, with increasing concern about pollution and modern farming methods, scarcity of butterflies is blamed on widespread use of insecticides or herbicides, on hedge-grubbing, ploughing of ancient meadows, or whatever is the current target for conservationists. I have no wish to defend irresponsible use of pesticides or thoughtless disruption of the countryside, but to blame these for low butterfly numbers is unjustified and probably inaccurate. Fluctuation in numbers from year to year is only to be expected in populations near the nothern limits of distribution, and the abundance, variety, rarities and range extensions recorded in the drought year are proof that nothing terrible has happened to our butterflies.

Gardens are particularly good places to see butterflies, because of their abundance of flowers. For nectar-feeding insects, they are rather like petrol stations for motorists – gaudy and conspicuous stopping places for replenishing fuel supplies. It is easy to assume that the few cabbage whites and small tortoiseshells regularly seen on buddleia are the same individuals from hour to hour and day to day, but marking and releasing show that this is not so. They are constantly on the move, just dropping in to top up their tanks. In extreme conditions, as was evident in 1976, local and woodland species, far from their usual haunts, and many migrants visit to feed. During the eight years 1972-79, we hand-netted 16,626 different butterflies of 21 species. While the bulk of the catch consisted of large and small cabbage whites, green-veined whites and small tortoiseshells, I never quite knew what would turn up next, a common blue, a small copper, or some new garden record. Yet my garden is in the busy suburbs of a large city, in a part of the Midlands that is not especially rich in butterflies; suburban gardens in other parts of the country, particularly in the southeast, would certainly have yielded more than 21 species in the eight-year period. Provision of abundant flowers for as long a season as possible seems to guarantee the presence of butterflies, and the unexpectedly large numbers I have recorded certainly dispel fears that they are on the decline.

There have, however, been changes in the status of some garden butterflies. Hand-netting is of no use for assessing changes in relative abundance of species, because it depends to some extent on inclination and effort. Although the Malaise trap catches few butterflies, compared, say, with hoverflies, it is consistent and non-selective, and gives an accurate picture of changes from year to year. There appears to have been a marked reduction in numbers of peacocks and small tor-toiseshells, since the boom years of 1975-76, suggesting that conditions have not been especially good for butterflies. Numbers of meadow brown and wall butterflies have also decreased, but these are butterflies of open sites, and it may be that they are recorded less often because the garden has become more overgrown. A rise in numbers of orange-tip butterflies may be a consequence of a general move into gardens and adoption of *Arabis caucasica* as a larval foodplant.

I make an effort to grow flowers that are regularly visited by butterflies, such as buddleia, pink stonecrop, Michaelmas daisies and other Compositae, privet, *Aubretia* and other Cruciferae, dwarf and herbaceous *Phlox*, and several species of *Dianthus*. An assortment of species of *Aster, Erigeron* and other North American meadow flowers, ensures that there is plenty of readily available nectar in late summer and autumn, when butterflies are abundant but there are few flowers available in the wild, and dead-heading of buddleia, perennial cornflower and other plants also prolongs the flowering season. The pungent flowers of privet and the yellow flowers of brassicas are especially attractive to butterflies, and it is no great hardship to leave hedges unclipped and allow a few cabbages to bolt.

The ideal would be to have butterflies breeding in the garden rather than dropping in to feed, but this is not easy to arrange. Cabbage whites are ubiquitous, and green-veined white and orange-tip females often lay in gardens, but other species rarely do so. The habitat requirements of egg-laying females of most species are very precise, and vegetation in general, sunshine or shade, terrain, shelter or exposure, are as important as presence of larval foodplants. Leaving a patch of nettles in a suburban garden, in the expectation that peacocks, small tortoiseshells and red admirals will breed, is a nice idea but little more than wishful thinking. I maintain a nettle patch, not as butterfly food, but for the other insects it harbours. It is equally misguided to purchase pupae from butterfly 'farms'. Despite the sales-talk, the butterflies that emerge will be disloyal; they may feed for a while at your garden flowers, but will then be off to join the vast floating populations of butterflies circulating through the gardens of suburbia. The best bet for having butterflies in the garden is provision and maintenance of abundant flowers at which they can refuel.

Hoverfly life-styles

August is the peak month for abundance and variety of hoverflies. They come in a range of colours, shapes and sizes: some species are tiny, dark and slender, some are robust and hairy like bees, others are banded with yellow and black like wasps. All feed at flowers, taking both nectar and pollen; some also exploit honeydew or visit rotting fruit for sweet juices, and I have caught a few species in traps baited with fish offal. Some species are predominantly nectar-feeders, others eat mainly pollen, and their tongues are modified accordingly. The drone fly (*Eristalis tenax*) and long-snouted *Rhingia campestris* visit flowers mainly for nectar; their tongues are long, and the lobed tip is relatively slender. Pollen-feeders, such as *Melanostoma* spp., *Syrphus ribesii* and *Episyrphus balteatus*, have short tongues and the lobed tip is broad, fleshy and sponge-like. *Metasyrphus corollae* and *Platycheirus* spp. take equal amounts of pollen and nectar, and have intermediate tongues. Nectar is sucked up the grooved tongue into the mouth, but pollen-feeding is a more complex process. Hoverflies appear to rub pollen masses between the fleshy lobes at the tip of the tongue, and suck separated grains, moistened with saliva, up the tongue groove. In all species, females take a higher proportion of pollen than males, the proteins it contains being essential for ovarian development. Males of some species, such as *Syrphus ribesii*, on the other hand, expend considerable energy on hovering in 'leks', or communal courtship territories, for which they need a high intake of nectar as fuel.

Unlike adults, hoverfly larvae use a variety of different foods, and live in a number of different sorts of microhabitats. Some eat plants, others eat animals, and either may serve as food while alive or after death. There are five major categories: plant-feeders, predators of aphids, feeders on dead organic material, feeders on tree sap and rotting wood, and scavengers in nests of ants, bees or wasps.

The majority of garden species and over 80 per cent of individuals caught in the Malaise trap, have larvae which prey on aphids and other sedentary plant-feeding bugs. The green, brown or whitish larvae, though slug-like, are certainly not sluggish, and can move with astonishing speed to capture aphids. An individual *Metasyrphus corollae* eats between 800 and 900 medium-sized aphids during its development. All the familiar yellow and black hoverflies, such as *Syrphus ribesii* and *Episyrphus balteatus*, together with slim, dark *Melanostoma* and *Platycheirus* spp., have aphid-feeding larvae.

The larvae of the next largest category – 18 species and 12 per cent of the total Malaise trap catch – are found in compost heaps, stagnant water or in other decaying organic material, such as faeces or carrion. Many species are primarily aquatic, although they fare as well in small puddles, such as found in knot-holes on tree trunks, or in wet decaying matter, as in the mud of pools and streams. The rat-tailed maggots of the drone fly live fully submerged, breathing air through a posterior tube (the 'rat-tail') which can be extended up to 14 centimetres. Drone flies sometimes lay their eggs in putrefying carcasses, and this is thought to be the basis for the account in the Book of Judges of how Samson found a swarm of bees and honey in the carcass of a lion, leading him to pose a riddle to his marriage guests: 'Out of the eater came forth meat and out of the strong came forth sweetness.' This ancient myth is perpetuated on tins of a proprietary brand of syrup, where the last phrase of the riddle is used as the caption for a picture of a dead lion surrounded by a swarm of insects. All the *Eristalis* are particularly fine creatures when viewed down a microscope. Even the smoothest-looking have an aura of fine, golden or tawny hairs, and they have decidedly aristocratic profiles, like those patrician ladies whose down-curving noses continue uninterrupted the positive line of their high foreheads. *Rhingia campestris* is also in this group, and *Syritta pipiens*, a common garden hoverfly, whose larvae develop in the compost heap. Adults are small and dark, with disproportionately thickened hind legs, and can often be seen feeding or resting on daisy-like flowers in the sun; males use flowers as courtship territories, defending them against intruders of the same or other species, by darting at them or 'buzzing' them in the air.

The other three larval feeding categories are less well represented. Most of the plant-feeders belong to three species which feed in bulbs as larvae, and reputedly cause considerable damage. Adults of the narcissus fly (*Merodon equestris*) are extremely variable in colour and pattern, although in general they are bee-like and furry. The inheritance of more than 30 different colour forms has been worked out by breeding experiments. Many of the forms resemble in colour pattern one or other of the species of bumblebees common in British gardens. Like the drone fly, they spend much time on flowers, even when not feeding, and the resemblance to bees is probably a protective adaptation. Males defend flowers as courtship territories in the same way as *Syritta pipiens*. The narcissus fly is a pest as far as commercial growers of daffodils are concerned; it is native to continental Europe, was introduced to Britain about 100 years ago, and is now also found commonly in the United States, and in Australasia and Japan. The lesser bulb flies, *Eumerus* spp., are quite unlike narcissus flies, being small and black; as adults they are inconspicuous, although in some years they are abundant in Malaise trap samples.

Rotting wood and sap runs on trees are not regularly available in gardens, and only a few individuals of five species whose larvae develop in such sites have been caught in the Malaise trap. Hoverflies whose larvae live in bee and wasp nests are represented by two species of *Volucella*, both large and robust. *V.bombylans* is furry and variable in colour pattern; it resembles at least two species of garden bumblebees, and I occasionally see it on flowers. *V.pellucens*, on the other hand, is black and shiny, with a striking white band at the base of the abdomen; I sometimes surprise one basking in the early morning sun on the loganberries, looking big, conspicuous and slightly sinister. *Volucella* larvae live as scavengers in bee or wasp nests, eating dead adults, larvae and pupae. They also stimulate host larvae to produce excrement, on which they then feed, and it is possible that they occasionally eat live larvae.

During their larval and adult life, hoverflies exploit a wide range of living spaces and food sources. The common denominator that draws them together is the dependence of adults on flowers for food, but egg-laying females and larvae occur in many different microhabitats. This, together with the variety of feeding habits, means that their relationships with their surroundings, and with other plants and animals, are extraordinarily diverse.

The web of life

Development of a garden as a habitat requires an understanding of the feeding relationships that bind its animals and plants into a community. All that green plants, the producers of the living world, require for growth and development are carbon dioxide, water, and a supply of nitrogen, phosphorus, magnesium, sulphur and other elements as salts absorbed in solution from the soil by their roots. Animals, fungi and most bacteria, however, need organic substances as food. They are consumers if they eat plants, animals or other organisms while they are alive, and decomposers if they feed on them after they have died. A particular sort of plant may therefore be the starting point for two parallel food chains, one of consumers and the other of decomposers. A quick look in the garden provides demonstration.

On my cabbages are several mealy clusters of cabbage aphids and among them are the predatory larvae of the black and yellow hoverfly, *Syrphus ribesii*. A small, pale, long-legged spider with a disproportionately large, globular abdomen, *Theridion ovatum*, has spun a frail web on an aphid-infested leaf, and has ensnared and killed an adult *S.ribesii*. It can deal with insects larger than itself, because as soon as a potential meal touches its web, the spider rushes from its retreat and flings sticky threads over its prey until it is firmly anchored. In the space of a cabbage leaf is a food chain in operation: cabbage – aphid – hoverfly – spider. In terms of feeding level, cabbage is the producer; cabbage aphids are primary consumers; hoverfly larve are secondary consumers; and the spider is a tertiary consumer.

When I harvest the cabbage, trim away the outside leaves and stalk, and discard them on the compost heap, another food chain comes into operation. Rain softens the cabbage leaves and they sink into the refuse, where mites and tiny insects nibble at them. Their corpses contribute to the organic melting-pot of the compost heap, on which brandlings and other earthworms feed; when they die, bacteria and fungi, which invade all the dead organic material in the compost heap, decompose their remains. Thus, nutrients and energy in the dead producer, cabbage leaves, pass along another food chain: scavenging mites and insects are primary decomposers; brandlings are secondary decomposers; and bacteria and fungi are tertiary decomposers.

In practice, neither consumer nor decomposer food chains are as discrete and straightforward as I have implied. A particular species of plant or animal may be eaten, alive or dead, by a variety of different sorts of organisms, and few consumers or decomposers specialize on one sort of food. Cabbages, for instance, are food for flea beetles, whitefly, spittlebugs, and caterpillars of moths and cabbage white butterflies; aphids are consumed by a variety of predators and parasites; and hoverflies are eaten by several sorts of birds, parasitized by ichneumonid wasps, and captured by social wasps as food for their larvae. Cabbage aphids are confined to brassicas, but *S.ribesii* larvae eat many different sorts of aphids on different species of plants, and spiders, such as *Theridion ovatum*, suck the juices from any small animal, including other spiders, that they can capture. Furthermore, consumer and decomposer food chains overlap; blackbirds eat caterpillars (consumers) as well as earthworms (decomposers), and bacteria break down the tissues of all dead organisms, be they cabbage, hoverfly, spider, bird, or another decomposer. Food chains branch and intersect to such an extent that a better representation of feeding relationships is a food web.

Another incident in the August garden illustrates the complexity of food webs. I pulled out some roots of marguerite daisies that were en-croaching on a path, to discover that they were enclosed in a nest of the black ant, *Lasius niger*. Clustered on the roots were unpigmented aphids that were evidently being tended and sheltered by the ants, who in turn were feeding on the aphids' honeydew. Ants as consumers are voracious predators, but when they feed on honeydew, which is a waste product, they are acting as decomposers. The ants began removing their own brood and the aphids to the dark, undisturbed recesses of their nest, but, as I stood watching, a song thrush flew down and ate the remaining aphids and ant brood. Thrushes are predators; in this instance, the prey were primary and higher order consumers, but garden thrushes are more often seen eating worms, which are decomposers.

A further difficulty in trying to slot animals into a particular consumer or decomposer level, is that individuals of some species change their position in food webs according to what food is available, like the thrush in the story above, or at different stages in their life histories. Larvae of the hoverfly, *S. ribesii*, as predators of aphids, are secondary consumers, but adults feed on pollen, on nectar, and on other sweet fluids. When adults feed at flowers, they are primary consumers, but when they lap honeydew, or imbibe juices from rotting fruit or animal remains, they are primary or higher order decomposers. I was watching *S. ribesii* and a *Vespula* wasp feeding on the nectar of fennel flowers, when the wasp caught the hoverfly and began to chew it up. Adult wasps, like hoverflies, are primarily flower-feeders, although they too feed at rotting fruit, but they catch insects for their larvae to eat, and can evidently adapt their behaviour rapidly to exploit what is available. Wasps usually operate as primary consumers, but their larvae are secondary or higher order consumers.

In the cabbage – aphid – hoverfly – spider food chain, spiders are tertiary consumers, and a wren or robin that ate the spider would be a fourth order consumer. It is possible to imagine a sixth feeding level – a cat, perhaps – but there is little scope for extending the food chain further. In practice, the vast majority of food chains on land consist of only three levels, producer, primary consumer, and secondary consumer; higher level consumers can be identified, but make up only a small fraction of the biomass (total quantity) of a community. Something evidently sets limits on the length of food chains, and it turns out to be the availability of energy. Although nutrients, such as carbon and nitrogen, are recycled, and pass along food chains again and again, energy goes only one way through a food chain or food web, and all is eventually converted into heat and lost to the atmosphere. A plant uses some of the light energy that it incorporates into sugars in its own life processes, and only 80 per cent or less is stored as chemical energy in its tissues. Herbivores and carnivores store only between five and 20 per cent of the energy content of their food in the chemical structure of their bodies; the rest is used in various cellular and bodily activities, and eventually lost as heat. By the time we get to fourth or fifth order consumers, such as robins or cats, the amounts of energy available to the feeding levels as a whole are infinitesimal. This is why top predators are always rare relative to herbivores, or, to be more accurate, why the biomass of top predators is small compared with that of herbivores. The

efficiency (or inefficiency) of energy transfer between feeding levels
limits the length of food chains.

Spiders – the master hunters

Since there is a finite limit to the number of successive consumer levels,
variety of predators in a habitat depends on the complexity of the food
web. The more different ways of making a living that are open to
predators, the more different sorts there are likely to be. In other words,
a varied producer level is likely to support many different consumer food
chains, and lead to the greatest possible variety of predators. The
extraordinarily high plant diversity established and maintained by
gardeners, generates a complex food web involving a rich diversity of
animals that eat other animals. Most are small, many are microscopic,
and few are conspicuous. But the garden harbours many different sorts
of one of the most varied and efficient groups of predators – the spiders.
Some operate by day, others by night. Some are active hunters, stalking
and pouncing on their prey; others lie in ambush and grab any small
animal that wanders within reach; a few fling restraining threads over
potential prey; and many construct webs, as snares or traps, reaching
their greatest complexity in the exquisitely constructed orb-webs of
Araneus spiders and their relatives. Spiders may not seem as dramatic as
killer whales chasing seals, lions stalking antelopes, or moray eels lying
in ambush in a coral reef, but within the one group of animals, and on a
small scale, is a whole range of different ways of catching prey, all
deadly, accurate, and extremely effective.

I have already described some of the spiders in my garden, but others
are more conspicuous in mid- to late summer, such as globular *Theridion*
with their scaffolding webs on cabbage leaves and other vegetation.
Harpactea are long-legged hunters with a markedly tubular grey abdomen. When hunting, they hold their front legs ahead of them, and
apparently use them to measure the dimensions of potential prey before
pouncing. I sometimes find *Harpactea* by day, but a torchlight excursion
at night is necessary to find another slim, yellowish hunter, *Clubiona*
terrestris, prowling amongst tree leaves. Yellow or white crab spiders,
Misumena vatia, lurk in ambush on yellow or white flowers, holding their
relatively enormous front legs out to the sides, like a crab's pincers, and
brownish *Xysticus cristatus* lies in wait amongst low vegetation. Crab
spiders are camouflaged, and pounce on unsuspecting insects, which
they restrain with their legs while delivering an immobilizing bite. Other
spiders hunt actively by day: little black and white jumping spiders,

known as zebra spiders, run around on the ground on hot afternoons, ready to jump considerable distances onto any suitable prey; and fast-moving, keen-sighted wolf spiders are on the prowl. Garden wolf spiders include close relatives of the notorious Italian tarantulas; they are fearsome hunters, but have neither large enough fangs nor sufficient poison to hurt a man. Female wolf spiders enclose their eggs in a covering of silk, and drag the egg-sac around attached to their spinnerets. When the eggs hatch, the babies are carried around on their mother's back for some days, until they are able to fend for themselves.

Some spiders are more in evidence in buildings than outside, and a night-time foray into the cobwebby garage by torchlight, disturbs a fawn, rather mouse-like spider prowling delicately along the cluttered shelves. This is *Drassodes lapidosus*, one of the cat-like hunters of the spider world; they stalk their prey slowly, until within striking distance, and then pounce with a sudden burst of speed and strength. They are a match even for spiders larger than themselves, for they combine stealth and speed with the strategy of looping a restraining band of silk around their struggling victim. Typically they construct their silken cells amongst clumps of dry grass or beneath stones, emerging to hunt at night, but their daytime retreats are easier to find and their hunting activities more open to observation within a building.

The most familiar and conspicuous spiders in August are those that build intricately structured orb-webs. The main spiral threads of the webs are sticky, and ensnare flies and other insects. The spider waits at the hub of her web, with her legs spanning the radial strands, or in a retreat under an adjoining leaf to which a signal thread runs. In response to vibrations set up by the struggles of an ensnared insect, she runs to where it is caught, bites it with her poison fangs, and proceeds to bind it; as a broad band of silk issues from her spinnerets, she rotates the captured insect, so that the silk wraps around it. The immobilized insect is again bitten, and then carried either to the hub of the web, or to the spider's retreat. Small prey parcels are carried in the jaw-like mouth appendages, but larger bundles are attached to the spinnerets and hauled along. Spiders can move freely across their webs, first because their legs are oily and slide off the sticky strands, and secondly because their feet bear hook-like claws which clamp firmly onto the delicate threads.

It is a fairly safe assumption that a spider sitting on or near to a web is a female. Garden spiders (*Araneus diadematus*), with a white cross on the fat abdomen, usually sit at the hub of their conspicuous webs, which they build across gaps between plants or fence posts; *A.cucurbitinus*, a little green spider, builds small webs that may span only a single, curled leaf; and a big, chocolate-coloured spider, *A.umbraticus*, builds her web on trees or fences, with her lair in a nearby crack into which she squeezes her flattened body. She pays little attention to her web by day, but at night ambles from her retreat to empty it of prey. A brightly patterned and pretty spider, *Meta segmentata*, slimmer and longer-legged than *Araneus* spiders, builds her inclined orb-webs on bushes, plants and fences, and waits either at the hub of the web or in a nearby retreat, clutching a signal thread. Males also spin silk, build webs, capture and ensnare prey, but they are much more mobile, and visit females' webs for mating. This is a hazardous undertaking, as they run the risk of being eaten, but this is usually avoided by such strategies as the male vibrating the web in a characteristic way as he approaches.

The changing scene

As a gardener, I am not especially busy in August, although broccoli seedlings are ready for planting out, the beans look as though they could do with some water, and it is time the old raspberry canes were removed, to let more light into the tangle of spotted dead-nettle, mint and feverfew below. Clipping the seed-heads from Marguerite daisies before they dry and fragment will reduce the amount of weeding needed next year, and it is well worth prolonging the flowering season of buddleia, by dead-heading, to encourage further butterfly visits. It might also be as well to stem the hungry tide of cabbage white caterpillars on the cabbages and other brassicas. Large cabbage white caterpillars are easy to locate and pick off, but small cabbage white caterpillars are more elusive, in keeping with their palatability; they are green and solitary, and tend to creep down between the leaves, out of sight. Chewed *Mahonia* leaves, obviously the work of caterpillars, attract my attention. The stick caterpillar of a peppered moth, and the fat green caterpillar of a bright-line brown-eye are exploiting unseasonal production of tender, new leaves, resulting from cutting back branches overhanging paths. *Mahonia* seeds excreted by blackbirds litter the paths, so it is no wonder that there are plants all over the garden.

A family of redpolls deftly and efficiently remove the flattened seeds from the small, gherkin-shaped fruiting bodies of the largest birch tree. On the steps beneath the tree is a mound of the three-toothed bracts, like tiny sharks' teeth, that enclosed the seeds in the fruit, and every time the wind blows, wafer-thin seeds work their way in through the cracks around the house windows. On hot afternoons, the only bird to be seen is a worn male blackbird, crouching, wings slightly spread, beak agape, on the edge of the lawn. Birds have no sweat glands, and their only means of lowering the body temperature is to increase the breathing rate so that more water evaporates from the linings of lungs and air sacs. When panting like this, a bird may look as though in great distress, but it is simply cooling down. Spotty, raucous, young starlings descend on the ripe elder berries, then move down to the lawn, where they strut gawkily to and fro, and there is a continuous scrabbling noise from the shrubbery, where blackbirds rootle among dead leaves. By mid-month, screaming parties of young swifts have made their last dare-devil swoop over the garden, and departed for Africa, leaving the air above strangely silent. Willow warblers, as a prelude to southward migration, are singing in half-hearted territorial defence, and summer is nearly over. Blackbirds have suddenly decided that the fruits of a small rowan are ready to eat, and a persistent female jumps awkwardly from the ground, again and again, to snatch individual berries from pendulent clusters drooping at the end of flimsy twigs. The berries are still pale orange, and I try one to see what the attraction is, but find it hard and astringent. Meanwhile, a snatch of the autumn song of a robin is an indication that males and females have established their individual winter feeding territories..

9

SEPTEMBER

Hungry hordes of caterpillars

The herbaceous borders are now at their most colourful. There is a wealth of perennial *Aster* and *Erigeron* of every hue, from clear, light blue and mauve to purplish-pink; African marigolds continue to produce blowzy citron and orange pom-poms, and the tall stems of goldenrod are still crowned with yellow haze. Michaelmas daisies and the other autumn-flowering composites revitalize the garden in late summer, and, together with buddleia, furnish abundant feeding opportunities for insects when there are few flowers in the wild. Red admirals, painted ladies, small tortoiseshells and peacocks add sparkle to tall clusters of Michaelmas daisies, to purple buddleia sprays, and to flat, low flower heads of pink stonecrop. They periodically inspect African marigolds, although the florets of fresh flowers are too densely massed for them to insert their slender tongues into the petal tubes with much success, and they prefer over-blown blooms.

The air above goldenrod and Michaelmas daisies scintillates with the flight of hoverflies, especially chunky, bee-like *Eristalis*, some large, a few quite furry, and many smaller *E.arbustorum*. Female *E.arbustorum* are black apart from narrow yellow edging to each abdominal segment, and are believed to mimic solitary bees, but males have pairs of conspicuous yellow, wedge-shaped marks, broadest at the outer edge, at the base of the abdomen, so that from a distance, especially when sittting on a yellow flower, they give the illusion of having a wasp-shaped black abdomen. Although past their best, sweet peas are attracting a great deal of attention from hoverflies. So intent are various species of dark *Platycheirus*, and yellow and black *Syrphus ribesii*, *Metasyrphus corollae* and *Episyrphus balteatus* on the drooping flowers, that I can approach close enough to see that all are females, and they are eating pollen from the exposed stamens. Sweet pea flowers are self-pollinated, and stamens and stigma remain tightly enclosed until the petals begin to wither. Consequently they retain an abundance of pollen, and form a reliable and valuable food source for female hoverflies requiring a pollen meal before egg-laying.

More house martins than I have seen all summer are zigzagging to and fro, with twinkling wings, above the garden. They twist and turn in pursuit of insects, as though following the invisible markers of some intricate slalom course. The arrival of so many twittering birds from colonies elsewhere is a sign that they are preparing to migrate southwards, and before long they will be off. The final departure of aerial feeders is an indication that the insect season has passed its peak. Many insect-eating birds are now on the move, and a willow warbler flits through the dense shrubbery outside the study window, while a chiffchaff sings fleetingly from the apple tree. Later, as evening falls, the dark silhouettes of bats are momentarily visible in the half light, hawking for aerial insects. As insect numbers decline, they find less and less to eat, and soon they will be going into hibernation.

Life and death amongst the vegetables
The runner beans are now tall, leafy, hung with green pods, and busy with insects. Leaves and stems are encrusted with black bean aphids, which have produced so much honeydew that the plants are sticky and black with mould growing on the sugar. Predatory hoverfly larvae browse on the aphids, and adult hoverflies and wasps visit constantly to feed on the honeydew. Extreme caution is necessary when picking beans, because honeydew ferments, producing enough alcohol for wasps to become too inebriated to fly, although quite capable of stinging if grasped along with a bean. Every morning at this time of year, I find the light trap full of wasps. They are a nuisance, as they catch and chew many moths, but all attempts to deter or distract them – such as a pot of jam set beside the trap – have failed. By the time the moths are released next evening, however, most of the wasps are dead, apparently unable to survive more than a few hours without an intake of energy-rich nectar or honeydew.

Wasps are still feeding larvae in the nest (which might explain their interest in the light trap), to judge by a spectacular encounter I witnessed one September day between a *Vespula* worker and a drone fly. I first noticed the hoverfly on the path with the wasp on its back. The two rolled around, wings buzzing, as the hoverfly attempted to take off and the wasp curved its abdomen round its captive, apparently trying to sting it. It was impossible to see whether the sting penetrated, but the wasp took a firmer grip with its legs, and bit through the bases of the fly's wings. As the fly continued to walk around, ocasionally rolling in an apparent attempt to dislodge its attacker, the wasp began to bite around the base of its abdomen, which after about half a minute was hanging by only a thin strand. The fly kept on walking around, and the wasp kept on chewing, reducing the contents of the fly's abdomen to pulp. The empty shell finally fell off, the wasp flew away with its load of minced meat, and the hoverfly, minus wings and abdomen, crawled into the vegetation beside the path, effectively dead though still managing to move its legs. I had to get down on my hands and knees to watch and the entire episode was over in a couple of minutes, but it was surely as violent and chilling as a lion's bloody onslaught on a zebra.

The cabbages are still the scene of many interwoven feeding activities. 7-spot ladybirds are bright splashes of colour amongst mealy aphids on the grey-green leaves, and ichneumonid wasps fidget to and fro, pausing every so often to drink honeydew. Many species that parasitize predatory hoverflies seek hosts in exposed, sunny sites, and are attracted to aggregations of aphids amongst which they eventually find a suitable recipient for their eggs. An egg remains quiescent in a hoverfly larva until it pupates, and then hatches. The parasitic wasp larva gradually consumes the contents of the pupa, so that finally a wasp not a hoverfly emerges. Bright green cabbage moth caterpillars lurk deep within the cabbage hearts, and in some years are particularly abundant. They start life on a whole range of different garden plants, but when nearly fully grown, wander off in search of dark, damp situations in which to continue feeding. Cabbages have been selected for just the character that suits them – formation of a tight, compact 'heart'.

Slugs and snails

The depredations of hungry slugs reduce me to tears, when they raze to the ground delphinium plants that I have lovingly and laboriously grown from seed. Soot keeps them away for a while, but as soon as it is dispersed by rain, they breech the flimsy defences. I eagerly seized on another suggested remedy, doubtful though I was of its effectiveness. Roughly-broken egg shells strewn around susceptible plants keep slugs away, because they cannot bring themselves to haul their soft little bodies across the sharp edges – or so the story goes. It ought not to work, because slugs are tough, and their slimy coating of mucus is defence against just such damage as egg shells might inflict, but for a while I thought the battle was won. The polite smiles of visitors, who heard my explanation for the conspicuous circles of broken egg shell in the flower bed, became easier and easier to tolerate as the delphiniums sprouted new leaves and gained height. But I had only won a brief skirmish, not the war. The broken shells are dispersed by rain and birds, and need gathering together and supplementing almost daily. In a spell of bad weather, I forgot to man the barricades, and the slugs rasped away at the tender stems, leaving collapsed, broken plants.

Slugs are not easy to identify. So far I have names for four species, but there are probably many more; the netted slug (*Deroceras reticulatum*) is the commonest slug in northeastern Europe, and the other three species are all regularly associated with gardens. They feed mainly on dead plant material, but the widespread species associated with man and his crops, also eat tender living plants, and three of my garden species are described in the field guide as 'notable' or 'major' pests. Slugs are, in effect, flattened snails that have almost or quite lost their shells; some species have a tiny shell at the hind end, but in most it is reduced to a thin plate embedded in the tissues or to a few chalky granules. Like snails, they feed by the rasping action of the radula, a strip of continuously growing horny tissue, covered with minute, sharp teeth, which is anchored in the floor of the mouth. Slugs and snails are efficient feeders, ingesting tiny fragments of plant material which they can digest completely as they are one of the few sorts of animals that produce cellulose-digesting enzymes. One of the reasons I am so plagued by slugs is that I spread large quantities of semi-decayed plant material on the soil surface with the compost. You might think that, with all that dead vegetation around, they would play fair and leave my plants alone. Curiously, they seem especially partial to a variety of thorn-apple (*Datura*), which I sometimes grow as an ornamental; its foliage is rich in poisonous alkaloids, which act on humans as a narcotic and induce a sensation of flying. I can only conclude that my hungry slugs are a gang of 'junkies', who aspire to be witches' 'familiars'.

Snails are not particularly abundant in my garden, whereas a friend living a few miles out in the country has common or garden snails (*Helix aspersa*) all over the place, even up the fruit trees. I sometimes find these beautiful large snails, with their delicately marked shells, near the rockery, but never in any numbers, although their English name is reputedly the origin of the everyday phrase 'common or garden'. Two species of tiny snails, one about eight millimetres in size, the other less than three millimetres, are quite common, but neither has an English name. The strawberry snail (*Trichia striolata*) frequents damp, moist vegetation, and can be a pest in strawberry beds, although I more often find empty shells. The shell is a flattened spiral, bearing regular striations, with a rather conspicuous circular depression in the centre of the coils. The shell of the garlic snail (*Oxychilus alliarius*) is a flat spiral, similar to that of the strawberry snail, but smaller, shiny and translucent, so that the dark body shows through. It is unmistakable when alive, for it smells strongly of garlic, especially when irritated.

Who's been nibbling at my plants?

Some caterpillars are discovered by detective work, as a consequence of following up such tell-tale clues as a chewed leaf, leaves rolled inwards and bound with silk, a scattering of fine frass on a path beneath overhanging vegetation, or uneven development of flower buds and seed-heads. Others are found by shaking out vegetation, or flower- and seed-heads, or by tapping tree branches sharply with a stick so that insects are dislodged and fall into an upturned, open umbrella. The study becomes a menagerie, with dozens of caterpillars in jars or plastic sandwich boxes, and each is supplied daily with fresh leaves from the plant on which it was discovered. Most ecologists dismiss gardens as barren habitats, on the assumption that introduced plant species are of no use as food to native herbivores. For moths, at least, nothing could be further from the truth.

I have found 33 species of moths feeding between them on 52 different species of alien garden plants including trees, herbaceous species, vegetables and herbs. Spotted dead-nettle from northern continental Europe is used by eight species, and purple-leaved Myrobalan plum from Persia, by nine, but, curiously, far and away the most heavily exploited alien is *Buddleia davidii* from China, which, unlike spotted dead-nettle and Myrobalan plum, belongs to a plant family unrepresented in the native flora of Britain. Stick caterpillars of the peppered moth, the ubiquitous and hungry caterpillars of cabbage moth, angle shades, dot moth and bright-line brown-eye, tiny, flower-feeding caterpillars of the double-striped pug, spotted caterpillars of the mullein moth, and many others, the vast majority of them polyphages, use it as a foodplant.

Most of the caterpillars using native garden plants are also polyphagous, but a few are limited in what they can eat: the early grey is restricted to honeysuckle, the herald to willows and poplars, and the spinach to the genus *Ribes*, which includes gooseberry, and black and red currant. Altogether, 27 native species are chewed by moth caterpillars, rose and hawthorn being the most popular, followed by shrubby cinquefoil, crack willow, brassicas, gooseberry, foxglove and nettle. In other words, those most heavily exploited as food are not for the most part 'weeds', but cultivated plants, which differ, to at least some extent, from the wild type. Most, such as roses and apples, have been selectively changed in flowering and fruiting characteristics, rather than in foliage, but the leaves of cabbage and other cultivated brassicas are very different in texture, growth form, and presumably in palatability, from wild cabbage.

The four species that I have reared from caterpillars using garden brassicas include two of the most catholic feeders, the cabbage moth and the angle shades. The cabbage moth is the most versatile, using 31 plants as diverse as marigolds, opium poppies, sweet peas and beauty bush; 21 of its foodplants are alien, including *Bryophyllum, Sinningia* (= *Glauxinia*), and black-eyed Susan (*Thunbergia alata*), grown as pot plants indoors. Presumably moths accidentally confined in the house off-loaded their eggs on the first plant they encountered, and the ability of the caterpillars to adjust to such exotic food emphasizes the versatility of their digestive systems. The angle shades is nearly as broad-ranging, with 26 foodplants, 22 of them alien, including buddleia, hollyhock and sage, and bias towards aliens is also clear in the varied diet of dot moth, bright-line brown-eye, lesser yellow underwing, and small angle shades. Polyphages can evidently adjust readily to unfamiliar plants, and the overwhelming impression is that moth caterpillars are well able to exploit the garden flora, especially introduced species and cultivars.

Many sawflies have greenish larvae that at first glance look like caterpillars, although they have more than five pairs of stubby 'legs' on the abdominal segments. The gregarious larvae of birch sawflies can be quite spectacular. They are green spotted with black, and I have found as many as 20 crowded on to a single birch leaf. By day they cluster motionless along the leaf edge, but when disturbed, elevate their hind ends in rigid curves, as though doing 'handstands'. The effect is startling, and presumably to a small bird, or other potential predator, most alarming. Sawflies are related to bees and wasps, but adults have flattened or tubular abdomens without a 'waist'. The Malaise trap catch indicates that there are quite a number of different sorts in the garden, but they are difficult to keep in captivity, and not all attempts to rear

PLATE 9   16 Blue sage flowers are adapted for pollination by bumblebees (see p. 103); magenta *Geranium cinereum* has readily accessible nectar. 17 Red valerian is a butterfly flower; the florets of perennial cornflower eject pollen onto insect visitors (see p. 107). 18 Buddleia acts like a magnet for butterflies, including migratory painted ladies (see p. 157).
19 *Sedum spectabile* attracts hoverflies, butterflies and many other insects.

larvae have been successful. Different species feed on birch, goose-berry, dog roses, hawthorn and willow, and another is particularly abund-ant on an alien crane's-bill, *Geranium cinereum*, turning the divided leaves into intricate lacework. The species on willow is familiar not in itself, but for what it does to the tree. An egg-laying female punctures willow leaves with her saw-edged ovipositor, depositing eggs singly within the leaf tissue. In response to the puncture, or to chemicals injected with the egg, the leaf develops a painful-looking red, bean-shaped gall. When the egg hatches, the larva feeds and grows within the gall, only leaving when it is ready to pupate.

Dividing the cake

Sawfly larvae, many sorts of moth caterpillars, aphids and other insects use willow leaves as food. Willow leaves are usually abundant, but should they become scarce relative to the numbers of individuals and species depending on them for food, willow-feeders might compete for available leaves. Competition between species arises when some essen-tial resource on which all depend is in short supply. However, unrelated animals differ in structure and life style. Aphids suck phloem sap, sawflies make galls and the larvae feed within them, and different species of moth caterpillar feed on different parts of a tree or at different seasons. Although they use the same plant for food, their ways of life differ and direct competition is unlikely. Even when a number of unrelated species openly compete for food, as when a variety of birds swoop onto a well-stocked bird table in winter, there is no fighting. Displacement of blackbirds by starlings, or of coal tits by greenfinches, is achieved by threat and submission. It seems to an observer as though there is tacit agreement, or at least acceptance, of who will get the major share. The least successful conserve their energies for seeking and exploiting an alternative food source, rather than wasting them on a dispute and risking injury and death.

But what happens when closely related and hence structurally similar species, belonging to the same genus, occupy the same habitat? Their life styles are bound to be similar, yet they succeed in living together without competition, because they have evolved crucial, if small, differ-ences in the ways in which they exploit the environment. It is as though they have partitioned the environment, the space, and the food it

PLATE 10   **20** Fully grown caterpillars of the elephant hawk moth may be brown or green (see p. 115). **21** An elephant hawk moth captured in the light trap (see p. 100) remains motionless when moved into the sunlight to be photographed. **22** 7-spot ladybirds lay clusters of eggs which hatch into active black larvae. Adults and larvae are predators of aphids. **23** This large cabbage white butterfly, probing a buddleia flower with its long tongue, has been caught and marked with a spot of red ink (see p. 60).

contains, between them, so that no two are ultimately dependent on the same essential resource.

My garden bird list includes five species of *Turdus*: blackbird, song thrush, mistle thrush, fieldfare and redwing. They are similar in size and structure, and all eat berries and other fruit, worms, snails, insects and spiders. Yet there are significant differences in their ecological requirements and in the ways in which they exploit their surroundings. Fieldfares and redwings are winter visitors, breeding in northern continental Europe, and mistle thrushes do not breed in my garden, requiring large trees in well-wooded areas. All three visit surburban gardens in winter to feed on fallen apples, and although they may rootle through leaf litter in hard winters when food is scarce, rarely compete with the predominantly animal-eating, resident blackbirds and song thrushes. Song thrushes eat snails whenever they are available, breaking the shells on 'anvil' stones, and are adept at locating and extracting earthworms from lawns, whereas blackbirds are opportunists, eating caterpillars when they are available, pouncing on worms when I dig or hoe, and waiting round the light trap in the morning to snap up any moths settled nearby. There is no evidence, even in winter when all five species feed in gardens, that they are in competition for food. On the contrary, characteristic differences in their ecological requirements are an evolutionary response to potential competition, which is thus averted.

Bumblebees are, for much of the year, the most conspicuous garden insects. The eight garden species differ in seasonality, in nesting and hibernation sites, in food sources and in feeding behaviour, effectively partitioning amongst themselves what this and neighbouring gardens have to offer. *Bombus pratorum* queens, black and yellow with a red tail, are the first to emerge from hibernation, often being on the wing in March; several other species appear in April, but *B.lapidarius* queens, black with a red tail, rarely emerge before late May or early June. Male *B.pratorum* are often produced as early as May, and colonies may finish in June, whereas those of tawny-brown *B.agrorum* and of *B.terrestris*, black and yellow with a brownish-white tail, run on into September and females are still on the wing in October. Early starters and late finishers can make the most of available food when few other species are around. Nest site preferences also differ. *B.ruderarius*, black with a red tail, and *B.agrorum* nest on the soil surface beneath clumps of grass or moss, whereas other species build nests at the end of disused mammal burrows. *B.hortorum*, one of the white-tailed black and yellow species, builds at the end of short tunnels, but *B.lapidarius* and *B.terrestris* use approach tunnels a metre or more in length. The early-nesting *B.prator-um* is an opportunist, using whatever sites are available, above or below ground. Hibernating queens also use different sites, *B.terrestris* burying themselves in soil beneath trees, whereas *B.lapidarius* queens burrow into well-drained banks. Thus there is considerable partitioning of the physical environment, in time and in space, between different species.

They differ in feeding behaviour, *B.agrorum* workers, for instance, rarely foraging further than 450 metres from their colony, whereas *B.lapidarius* workers may collect food at sites more than a kilometre away. They tend to visit different flowers, largely because tongue length differs between the species. Although bumblebees usually collect food from flowers with tubes a few millimetres shorter than their tongues, tongue length places a limit on depth of flower tube from which nectar can be extracted. *B.lucorum*, black and yellow with a white tail, and *B.terrestris* have the shortest tongues, 10 millimetres or less in length, and feed conventionally at flowers with rather short petal tubes, such as white clover and heather. Both are nectar thieves, which bite holes in the bases of deep flowers to extract nectar, and they are the main bumblebee exploiters of honeydew. At the other extreme are two white-tailed black and yellow species, *B.ruderatus* and *B.hortorum*, with tongues of 20 millimetres or more, which only feed at flowers with deep petal tubes, such as red clover. They have access to nectar that other species cannot reach, and never eat honeydew or rob flowers of nectar, although their jaws are quite strong enough to bite holes in petals. *B.agrorum* is intermediate in every respect; its tongue is 11-14 millimetres long, it feeds at flowers, such as bird's-foot-trefoil (*Lotus corniculatus*), with nectar at an intermediate depth, and uses both red and white clover. There are also specific preferences in feeding sites. *B.lucorum*, for instance, tends to feed at exposed flowers, whereas *B.pratorum* visits flowers sheltered and shaded by vegetation. The net result is that the relationships of the eight garden species to their environment differ sufficiently for all to be accommodated in the same area.

Moving with the seasons

An unexpected visitor, a red *Sympetrum* dragonfly, zigzags to and fro over the lawn bed for a minute or two, alights briefly on an African marigold, and is off again. Dragonflies are hunters, catching insect prey in flight, but their larvae are aquatic, and they are rarely seen far from water. A few species, however, appear to undertake mass movements.

Large numbers of *Sympetrum* have occasionally been recorded on the southeastern coast of England, apparently immigrants from continental Europe; there are records of large-scale southward movements in France and the Pyrenees in autumn, and I have seen many dragonflies, including a species of *Sympetrum*, in arid country on the southwestern tip of Portugal in September. The inference is that they are migratory, although little is known for certain about their movements. However, many of the species of insects, such as red admirals, painted ladies and silver Y moths, that exploit the profusion of garden flowers in late summer and early autumn are undoubted migrants. Like swifts, willow warblers and other migratory birds, they move north to exploit the abundance of food available in the northern summer.

Migration is a predictable, regular movement of a population, usually annually, to and from a breeding ground. It is most familiar in birds, where the same individual undertakes both outward and return journeys. The generation time of insects is short by comparison, and different individuals are involved on the two stages of the round trip. Moreover, there may be breeding all along the route, so that a wave of successive generations ebbs and flows south and north. Insect migration can be viewed as a population strategy for following the north-south shift during the year of seasonally available food for larval stages.

Red admirals occur in North Africa, the Canaries and Azores, throughout Europe, and in Asia Minor, but the population shrinks away from the northeast of the range in autumn, and expands to occupy the whole area in spring. In North Africa they fly and reproduce throughout the northern winter; in southern Europe adults remain active all winter but do not breed, and the few that stay in Britain hibernate. Migration has been observed in a northerly or north-northwesterly direction from March to mid-August, and in a southerly or south-southwesterly direction from mid-August to November. Those seen in England in spring are hibernated individuals, but these are soon joined by immigrants, and a single summer generation is produced, using nettle as a larval foodplant. In the autumn, most fly south to southern Europe and perhaps on to North Africa, whereas a few stay around, feeding on late flowers and basking in the autumnal sunshine before hibernating. They are strong, fast fliers, travelling by dusk as well as in daylight, and may cover several hundred kilometres a day. Consequently they overfly large tracts of land when migrating, and may suddenly arrive in places far from where they were last observed.

Painted ladies, too, are strong, fast fliers that move north in leaps and bounds. They are almost worldwide in distribution, but those we see in England are part of the population extending across northern Europe and south through the Mediterranean countries to North Africa. Good years for painted ladies follow population explosions to the south which have forced them to travel north in search of breeding sites and of nectar as fuel to sustain their active flight. Northward movement has been observed in North Africa from March onwards, and in the Middle East from April until September. All movement observed in western Europe in spring and summer has also been in a northerly or north-northwesterly direction. In Britain and the rest of western Europe, they fly south or south-southwest from the end of August through the autumn, and in the Middle East all movements observed from September until April have been southwards. Immigrants are unlikely to reach Britain before June, although the occasional strong southerly airstream in winter or spring may lead to painted ladies, and other migrants, being whisked north out of season. Spring sightings always follow unusual weather to the south; there is no record of hibernation. A single generation is produced in the British summer, using thistles as larval foodplants. Newly emerged painted ladies, on the wing in late August and September, are fresh and colourful compared with the worn, faded immigrants seen earlier in the summer. They start moving south at the end of August, and probably pass through three generations before moving north again.

The scale and extent of the northern movement of red admirals and painted ladies varies from year to year; some reach us every year, but numbers in Britain fluctuate considerably. Mass movement of clouded yellow butterflies is even less predictable. Occasionally they arrive in great swarms on southern and eastern coasts of England and gradually diffuse through the country as far north as Orkney and Shetland, but in most years few, if any, arrive. Some make the return journey, but none survive the British winter, and their presence is dependent on repeated immigration. The situation is similar in the silver Y moth, which also occurs throughout Europe to North Africa. Unlike most moths they are active by day as well as at night, and have been seen migrating north-northwest in spring and summer. Two or three generations are produced during the English summer, the caterpillars feeding on low-growing plants including many grown in herbaceous borders, and by late summer, in some years, flower beds are alive with active, fast-flying adult moths. Neither they nor their young stages can survive the English winter, and they fly south again in autumn. Like red admirals and painted ladies, they experience a mass population drift north in summer and south again in autumn.

A number of species of southern European and African hawk moths occasionally arrive in England in large numbers, but it is an irregular and unpredictable northward movement, and is perhaps best regarded as a one-way irruptive movement from an area of high population density. Hawk moths are powerful fliers, and are well known as migrants in many parts of the world. The bright little hummingbird hawk, with its large eyes and bird-like 'tail', is common in southern Europe, and regularly moves north in summer, although the numbers arriving in England vary greatly from year to year. Most move south again in autumn, and there are only a few records of them hibernating in Britain. It is a safe assumption that any seen in summer are immigrants. A few death's-head hawks and convolvulus hawks reach England in most summers, migrating north from southern Europe and Africa, and every ten to fifteen years there are quite large influxes. They cannot over-winter here, and many presumably fly south in the autumn. The arrival of brightly-marked striped and silver-striped hawks from Africa is even less predictable, although they move up through Europe in most years, and a few occasionally reach Britain.

The situation of those hoverflies that regularly undertake mass movements is much more difficult to resolve. The species most conspicuously involved are *Syrphus vitripennis* (hard to distinguish from *S.ribesii*), *Metasyrphus corollae*, *Episyrphus balteatus* and *Scaeva pyrastri*. All feed as larvae on aphids, a seasonal and unpredictable food supply, and, unlike many other aphid-feeders, pupate on completing their larval development, giving an autumn emergence of adults. There are many recorded observations of southward movement in autumn, particularly of *E.balteatus* through mountain passes in the Pyrenees, though few of northward movement in spring. The evidence for northward movement is mainly circumstantial: sudden appearance of large numbers in southern and eastern England, and drifts of dead hoverflies washed up on beaches. As with dragonflies, it remains an open question whether hoverflies are truly migratory, or whether, like many hawk moths, they make irruptive movements when numbers are high and food becomes scarce.

Harvest time

The entire garden seems to be ripening in the golden September sun. Crisp, flushed apples weigh down the gnarled, black branches of the

Worcester Pearmain. It is apples for everyone, again and again, for they do not keep and are best eaten straight from the tree. The bramble is laden with glistening, deep purple blackberries, the biggest and juiciest tantalizingly high on arching, prickly stems. The briar glows with rose-hips, clusters of deeper red haws hang from hawthorn, and plump, golden fruits enliven the thorny tangle of a climbing floribunda rose. Bittersweet, or woody nightshade, sprawling over the sombre growth of Lawson's cypresses, is spangled with shiny red berries, and must be clipped on the road side to ensure that none of the inviting fruits is within reach of a child. Tall fennel plants are crowned with stiff circlets of individually-stalked, flat seeds, peppery in taste, which were once widely used to alleviate hunger. These are the 'Meetin' seeds', which Puritans chewed to fortify themselves during long sermons on forbearance. I use the feathery leaves to add pungency to salads and sauces, ever mindful that in medieval times fennel was claimed to be 'the best way to keep witches from one's door'.

Birds become more conspicuous as they take advantage of the abundance of seeds and fruits. A blue tit stuffs itself with the grey-blue berries of flowering currant, and blackbirds soon strip the bushes of the rest. Linnets fly to and fro, and goldfinches, dapper and colourful as guardsmen, prize seeds from between the spikes of teasel heads. A male house sparrow, emulating the redpolls, though clumsy by comparison, perches precariously on a drooping birch spray, tearing at the seed clusters and dropping more than he eats. Other sparrows on the ground beneath, exploit his carelessness, and hop about pecking up scattered seeds. After they have gone, an unobtrusive hedge sparrow, ever the opportunist, discreetly gleans what is left.

Early morning mists blanket the garden, screening the sun, and the autumn flowers are sodden with dew. Several *Bombus agrorum* have spent the night nestled into aster flowers, and are still too sleepy to move, although as I approach a male raises one hind leg stiffly, apparently in nonchalant salutation. Spider webs bedewed with moisture are silvery in the hazy light. The tall stems of marguerites and tarragon, and the entire rockery, are covered with a jumble of small sheet webs, looking like flat-roofed villas perched on a steep hillside. Drifts of fallen leaves, from birch, privet, buddleia, mock orange, and many other trees and shrubs, accumulate in sheltered corners, an unwelcome reminder of the advancing season.

10

OCTOBER

The feast at the fallen fruit

Looking back over my diary of garden events, I realize, yet again, how misleading it can be to link biological events or gardening tasks with a particular month. In some years, summer is effectively over by early September, and by the end of the month, days start dark and cool, the garden is blowzy and untidy as Michaelmas daisies and goldenrod tumble higgledy-piggledy, the lawn stops growing, and paths gleam darkly with wet leaves and algal slime. But autumn is not always so gloomy. In other years, summer seems to stretch on and on. The sun is warm, if low in the sky, butterflies, bumblebees and big hoverflies bask and feed on late flowers, and winter seems comfortingly remote. In these Indian summers, gardens keep on growing, the lawn needs frequent cutting well into October, and there is enough heat in the sun for me to work up quite a sweat pushing the mower.

As I sweep dead leaves from the paths, I come across an amazing number of seedlings of birch, Lawson's cypress and other plants, snuggling into sheltered crevices between paving slabs. A dead wood mouse, the third record, is an unexpected find, for the garden is remarkably free of mammals, apart from trespassing cats and dogs. From time to time I see bats silhouetted against the sky on summer evenings, hedgehogs occasionally appear at dusk and amble across the lawn or rummage around in the compost heap, and grey squirrels visit from time to time and run nimbly along the fences, especially in winter. I once surprised a small mouse, probably a house mouse, quietly nibbling at a stock of dried guinea-pig food in an outhouse, and found another, dead, in the garage. A dead, and partially eaten, short-tailed vole appeared, one late August morning, by the compost heap. It had perhaps been dropped by a kestrel, and was the centre of attention for dozens of wasps that eagerly chewed at the exposed flesh. That, however, is the sum total of garden mammals, unless you count my belief that I smelt a fox early one morning.

This is a good time of year to have an onslaught on invasive pink oxalis, while the cluster of little bulbils is still attached to each fleshy, grey tap root and it can be eased in one piece from the damp soil. These are definitely not for the compost heap, as the separated bulbils will each sprout into new plants wherever compost is spread. A more enjoyable and constructive job is harvesting seeds for planting next year: pot marigold, hollyhock, nasturtium, dwarf convolvulus, sage, nicotiana and many others. Removing husks and bracts, and collecting together the seeds is time-consuming, but eminently satisfying. It is several years since I purchased seeds of nicotiana, or of dwarf convolvulus, two of my favourite garden flowers, and marigolds and hollyhocks were inherited from previous householders.

Large *Eristalis* hoverflies are active on sunny days, and the occasional large cabbage white, peacock, small tortoiseshell or red admiral, but the insect season is effectively over, and the Malaise trap comes down at the end of the month. Although some years there is an abundance of flowers, there are few insects to exploit them. One October day in 1979, aware that the garden was unusually colourful, I listed the plants in flower, and was amazed at the number: African marigolds, annual asters, *Aubretia*, borage, buddleia, dwarf convolvulus, perennial corn-flower, evening primrose, fennel, feverfew, foxglove, *Fuchsia*, golden-rod, honeysuckle, larkspur, lavender, marguerites, Michaelmas daisies, montbretia, nicotiana, pansy, roses, snapdragon, spotted dead-nettle, pink stonecrop, sweet pea and blue *Veronica*. Many were well past their prime, so that the garden looked illkempt, but the few insects still around enjoyed an eleventh-hour feeding bonanza. Some late flowering is in response to pruning and dead-heading, or to damage caused by insects or weather, and a list like this could not be made in October every year, but it emphasizes the variability of actual timing of seasons from one year to the next.

Eating fruits and seeds

Beneath the apple tree's spreading branches, paths, soil and compost heap are littered with fallen fruit in varying stages of damage and decay. For a few weeks, this becomes the busiest part of the garden, humming with insects. As I pick each damaged apple from the path, a wasp emerges belligerently from an excavation in the mushy, brown interior.

A red admiral probes fermenting pulp with its long proboscis, blackbirds peck at bruised, split fruits, and a host of other animals, large and small, avail themselves of this seasonal concentration of food.

In the language of botanists, a fruit is the structure that develops to enclose ripe seeds, consisting of the thickened ovary wall and neighbouring parts of the flower. The fruit wall of many plants becomes dry and hard; in others it remains fleshy and soft, and in some it becomes juicy, sweet and brightly coloured. It is the latter which are popularly known as fruits, and this is how I use the word here. There is nothing fortuitous or philanthropic about the way some plants enclose their seeds in succulent flesh. The evolutionary reason for a plant diverting valuable resources into fruit tissues is to ensure dispersal of the seeds. Juice, concentration of sugars, palatability, and attractive, conspicuous colours are adaptations for increasing the chances that the seeds are ingested by an animal. Animals that further the evolutionary aims of a plant are those that regurgitate or defaecate intact, viable seeds some distance away from the parent plant with which they might otherwise compete for space, light, water and nutrients. Thus, when blackbirds in my garden eat the berries of flowering currant, *Mahonia*, holly, bittersweet, and blackberries, they are acting as legitimate fruit-eaters. The regular appearance of seedlings of these plants everywhere in my garden is proof that blackbirds are successful as agents of seed dispersal, and that the plants' investment in fruits has been worthwhile.

Apart from certain ants, which collect seeds of dwarf gorse and violets, eat the oily caruncle (a fleshy outgrowth), and then discard viable seeds, legitimate fruit-eating is confined to vertebrates, large enough to swallow whole fruits, or large chunks of them. In my garden it is probably only birds that fulfill this role, although many mammals function as dispersal agents, and, in some parts of the world, reptiles, such as the giant tortoises of the Galapagos Islands. Man plays a part too, as evinced by the many tomato seedlings that grow on sewage farms. Blackbirds are undoubtedly the dominant legitimate fruit-eaters in my garden, but they are not dependent on fruit. Like other species of thrushes such as fieldfares and redwings, they are opportunist fruit-eaters, exploiting fruit as food if and when it is available. Indeed, they could not manage on fruit alone, for it contains little other than water, sugar and vitamin C. In tropical forests, however, some sorts of birds have become specialist fruit-eaters. So close is the association between plants and birds, that the plants have evolved highly nutritious, though not particuarly succulent, fruits, full of proteins and fats as well as carbohydrates, and the birds eat nothing but fruit. Such inter-dependence is possible in tropical forest, where trees and shrubs of one sort or another bear fruit all year round, but could not develop in a temperate area where fruiting is a strictly seasonal phenomenon.

When a blackbird pecks at the flesh of windfalls beneath the apple tree without swallowing any seeds, its activities amount to vandalism. The seeds are unharmed, but they are not dispersed, and fruit that should have been both attraction and reward for a dispersal agent, is spoilt and damaged. But the sorts of apples that we grow in our gardens and orchards, have been selectively bred for size and succulence since Roman times or even earlier. Wild crab apples, from which they have been developed, are small enough for a blackbird to swallow whole. Many fruit-eating animals are unmitigated vandals: codling moth cater-pillars that excavate brown burrows in apples; red admirals, silver Y moths and wasps that suck the juices oozing from ripe blackberries; and slugs that grate and gouge their way into strawberries and tom-atoes. Other fruit-eaters are out-and-out thieves, eating the seeds as well as the surrounding fruit, although this is a relatively rare phenom-enon in gardens. Small mammals eat berries and other fruit to get at the seeds, although wood mice carefully pick them out and discard the pulp!

Seed-eaters as such pose a real threat to plants, because they destroy entire individuals. Goldfinches on teasel, linnets on thistles, greenfin-ches on sage, and redpolls on birch are seed predators, eating vast numbers of individual plants before they have even germinated. In contrast to fruit, seeds are rich in proteins and fats, intended for the growth and development of the embryo plant. Like eggs they make a meal, whereas fruit is little more than a tempting, sweet drink. Birds are the most conspicuous seed predators in gardens, but mice and squirrels gnaw at nuts and seeds to extract the kernels, beetles, particularly weevils, consume vast numbers, and slugs and caterpillars chew peas and other legumes in the pod. Paradoxically, seed predators may also, to some extent, act as agents of dispersal. Greenfinches and other birds scatter seeds as they feed, ants store in their underground nests more than they eat, and not all squirrels' caches of winter food are used. Nevertheless, some plants have developed defences against seed pre-dators, such as massively hard seed coats. The unfortunate conse-quences of children mistaking laburnum pods for peas are all too well known. Laburnum is native to tropical America, where it evolved toxic alkaloids in the seeds as chemical defences against tiny, seed-eating beetles. Though serious, it is incidental that the seeds are also poisonous to man.

In defence of pests

Striving for perfection in the garden produces a sort of random intolerance to judge by an adage quoted on *Gardeners' Question Time* on BBC radio: 'If it moves slowly enough, step on it; if it doesn't, leave it – it will probably kill something else.' Gardeners tend to regard as pests any animal that is 'in the wrong place' or that interferes, in however small a way, with attempts to grow the plants of their choice, whether they be roses or carrots. In other words, a pest is a subjective and egocentric human concept, not a biological category.

An acceptable and workable ecological definition of a pest is 'a species that makes it difficult for man or one or more of man's associates to survive and flourish', which can be applied with equal justification to plants and animals, although the term is popularly restricted to animals. The average gardener's concept of a pest is even more subjective than the ecological definition. He, or she, decides not only what plants will grow and where, but also who may or may not share his garden, and who will eat what. The goal is not so much management as total domination, but this is wellnigh impossible to achieve. I have never met a gardener who wanted to eradicate ladybirds, hoverflies, blue tits or thrushes. But ladybirds and hoverflies eat aphids, blue tits eat caterpillars, and thrushes eat snails. Use of insecticides and other pesticides, against aphids, caterpillars and snails, endangers well-loved garden animals, even the swifts feeding overhead on aerial plankton, because it depletes or contaminates their food supply. Sometimes the results of interfering with the complex inter-relationships of a garden are unforeseen, as when a persistent poison becomes concentrated as it is passed along a food chain. More often they are glossed over, as in a self-congratulatory advertisement for an aphid poison, harmless to ladybirds, which makes no suggestion as to what the ladybirds might eat when the aphids have gone.

A curious feature of beliefs about pests is that they incorporate other prejudices. An eighteenth-century gardener was advised to place wind-breaks to the east, because caterpillars and other pests were 'borne in great clouds on the east wind'. Commercial fruit-growers remain convinced, despite evidence to the contrary, that the bullfinches, which strip their trees of buds in winter, are immigrants from continental

Europe. Abundant animals that eat crops or treasured plants are assumed to be aliens, which is, perhaps, a justification for eradicating them. But a gardener who eradicates all the plant-feeders in his garden will destroy the whole food web, and end up with a lifeless plot. If he has pests, he does so from choice, and can get rid of them instantly by adopting a more tolerant attitude. In a colourful, rich and interesting garden, there is a place for everything – or almost everything. I view cats with horror, and give them a deterrent taste of an effective pesticide – a large, well-aimed stone.

Adjusting to the seasons

Gardeners adjust their plans and activities to the time of year, and even the least active city-dweller is aware of the changing seasons. We take for granted blooming of daffodils in spring and of Michaelmas daisies in autumn, a strawberry season and a 'conker' season, autumnal leaf fall, the arrival of swifts and house martins in early summer and their departure later in the year, spring nesting of blackbirds and song thrushes, and hibernation of peacock butterflies and queen wasps. Although seasonal changes in our weather are nowhere near as extreme as in land-locked continental areas, where temperatures soar in summer and plummet in winter, or in tropical areas, where torrential rains alternate with drought, their effect on plants and animals is pronounced. Winter is characterized by short, cool days and summer by long, warm days. Flowering and fruiting seasons, leaf fall, nesting seasons, migration and hibernation are geared to mean temperatures, but above all to daylength.

Conditions in winter are generally unsuitable for plant growth and reproduction, which have, therefore, to be fitted into a period of about seven months, from April to October. The rate of all chemical reactions, including photosynthesis, increases with temperature. As the weather warms up in spring, annual seeds germinate, deciduous trees put on a new covering of green leaves, perennial root stocks sprout, and evergreens resume growth. Photosynthesis occupies a greater proportion of each twenty-four hours as days lengthen, further boosting plant growth. Flowers are produced, and in the warmth of summer fruits develop and seeds ripen, but not all species of plants flower and fruit at the same time. Temperature and daylength are important, but so are other factors. Some types of plants depend on particular weather conditions, such as wind, for pollination and seed dispersal, and it may be advantageous for this reason to flower or produce seeds at certain times of year. On the other hand, many species exploit animals as pollination and dispersal agents, and their availability has probably been as important as weather in the evolution of flowering and fruiting seasons. Synchronization of the activities of pollinating insects and flowering plants is essential for survival of both.

Invertebrates, from insects and spiders to slugs and snails, and 'cold-blooded' vertebrates, such as newts, cool, and hence slow down, as temperatures drop, and most become torpid and inactive. In other words, most of the garden's inhabitants are unable to move freely for part of the year. Seasonal fluctuations in availability of food have an even greater effect. Green leaves, nectar, seeds and fruit, are unavailable as food for much of the year, and so are the majority of insects and other small animals. Even birds and mammals that remain active in gardens in winter may have a lean time, and many of the most widespread and abundant, such as starlings and grey squirrels, are to some extent dependent on food provided by man, whether intentionally or not. For most garden animals, there is only a limited period each year when food is plentiful and easily acquired, and which is therefore optimal for raising young. The evolutionary response of animals to marked seasonal variations in suitability of conditions for breeding and, indeed, for any sort of activity, has been first, to restrict production of young to the time of year when most food is available for them, and secondly, to elaborate strategies for avoiding exposure to difficult climatic conditions. The first has led to seasonal breeding, and the second to migration and hibernation.

Producing young at the season when most food is available for them is not as straightforward as might at first appear. Good feeding conditions cannot be used as a signal for the onset of breeding because the preliminaries, such as courtship and mating, selection or preparation of breeding site, egg production, and growth and development of embryos, take time. If a bird, or insect, or snail, only became interested in breeding when conditions were optimal for the young, they would have lost their chance, for the situation would be quite different by the time their reproductive activities had produced results. Consequently, animals have evolved responses to predictable seasonal events, which may have nothing to do with optimal feeding conditions for the young, but act simply as convenient environmental triggers to get breeding started far enough ahead.

Consider garden spiders (*Araneus diadematus*): males and females mate in August, females leave their webs to lay their egg clusters in

September or October, but the babies do not hatch until May, when it is warming up and there is an abundance of tiny flies, aphids, and other small food items for them to eat. The young are produced in May because food is abundant, and they have all summer for growing up. This is the evolutionary reason, but it can only be achieved by adults responding initially to events in the preceding August. Since garden spiders live for only one season, their internal clocks are programmed for less than twelve months. By August, their clocks have probably ticked round to the point where mating is bound to be the next event, but the immediate reason for the onset of breeding may well be consistent incremental decrease in daylength.

For a bird, such as the swift, reproduction is complicated by the need to travel thousands of miles to and from a breeding ground. Young swifts are in the nest being fed by their parents in July, when aerial plankton is dense and rich. To achieve this, the adults have left tropical Africa in late March or early April, arriving locally in mid-May; they have paired off, mated, selected nesting holes, and produced two or three eggs, all in advance of optimal feeding conditions. The ultimate, or evolutionary, reason for arriving here in May is to get the young in the nest by July, but the immediate reason, or environmental trigger, for the chain of events is quite different. In the first instance, there is a regular, annual cycle in the adults' physiological state, a sort of inbuilt calendar. By the end of March, they have replaced physical resources drained by last year's nesting and southward migration. Their gonads are ready again to produce eggs or sperm, and are flooding each bird's system with sex hormones, which probably get it all geared up to go when it gets the right signal. The trigger for northward migration, the first step in the chain of events, has not been identified for certain, but it could be the onset of seasonal rains in the tropics, or an associated increase in availability of aerial insects.

Decreasing daylength has been identified, by experiment, as the signal used by birds for southward migration in late summer and autumn. The evolutionary reason for insect-eating birds spending the northern winter in the tropics is that there would not be enough food to sustain them here, but they leave before conditions deteriorate. Any that stayed behind would die, whereas those that travel south in winter survive, and so there is strong selection for migration, triggered by shortening days. But long-distance travel is only one possibility for avoiding the northern winter with its low temperatures and food scarcity. For most animals, migration would be impractical, if not impossible, and they have developed various ways of shutting down for the winter. Peacocks, small tortoiseshells, a few other species of butterflies, and various sorts of robust insects, like wasps and bumblebees, hibernate as adults, and some moths pass the winter as caterpillars, and a few hoverflies as larvae. A far more common strategy, however, is to over-winter in an immobile, non-feeding stage of the life cycle. For many animals, from spiders to aphids, this means passing the winter as eggs, which only hatch when things warm up in spring, but those insects that undergo complete metamorphosis in their development have another possibility, the pupa, and this is how cabbage white butterflies, the majority of moths, and many flies, solitary bees and wasps, and beetles spend the winter. Eggs and pupae neither move nor feed, and in these forms insects or other animals can sit quite happily for months waiting for conditions to ameliorate; energy expenditure is minimal, and they are relatively well insulated from events in their surroundings.

Despite adaptations which guarantee an appropriate response to the changing seasons, animals retain a certain amount of flexibility in coping with unusual weather. It is as though, in extremity, they can over-ride their programming. Northbound swifts, for instance, may 'hold' over continental Europe, or even double back for a while, if they meet bad flying and feeding weather. In sunny, warm autumns, red admirals and other butterflies are on the wing later than usual, postponing migration or hibernation. Limited adjustments in the timing of events are essential to survival, but they remain secondary to adaptations to the usual and predictable pattern of the seasons.

The birth and death equation

While washing the dishes one evening, I suddenly noticed a raft of a hundred or more darkening moth eggs on a single leaf of a basil plant in a pot on the kitchen window-sill. Some had hatched, the rest were about to do so, and I moved the leaf and its occupants to a plastic sandwich box which, by next day, housed a creeping, dangling multitude of tiny caterpillars. I took a gamble on them being cabbage moths or something equally polyphagous, and supplied an alternative foodplant, which they accepted – just as well, for even if I had been prepared to sacrifice all my basil, there was insufficient for such a hungry horde. Every female cabbage moth lays at least a hundred eggs. If all survived to adulthood, we should be brushing aside and trampling on cabbage moths everywhere we went. Assuming they breed only once a year, producing equal numbers of males and females, and making modest claims for fertility, a pair could become a hundred in the second year, 5,000 in the third, 250,000 in the fourth, twelve-and-a-half million in the fifth year, and in no time at all, we should be inundated with cabbage moths.

Less mind-boggling, though just as dramatic, is the potential for growth of populations of larger garden animals, such as blackbirds. Garden blackbirds more than one year old have a clutch size of three or four, and make at least three nesting attempts in a year, although first year birds tend to lay smaller clutches and make fewer nesting attempts. Even allowing for losses to nest predators, such as crows, pairs in their second year may raise ten or more fledglings with an average of more than six. One year's nesting efforts by a male and female could add a minimum of three breeding pairs to the population. The next generation is potentially at least nine pairs, then twenty-seven, then eighty-one, and so on; if all survived, our gardens would be overrun by blackbirds. It is evident that this does not happen. There is enormous potential for population growth, whether in cabbage moths, blackbirds, or any other organism, but it is rarely realized. All animals and plants produce as many young as possible under prevailing conditions, yet numbers remain more or less the same from one year to the next.

Since birth rates are so high, the inescapable conclusion is that regulation of numbers is by death. This basic truth is often difficult to accept, because man, in the short term, has circumvented natural regulation of his numbers by altering his relationship to his surroundings. Nevertheless, the vast majority of the young of most species do not survive to reproductive age. The environment can accommodate and support only a certain number of a particular sort of animal or plant; its carrying capacity for each species is fixed. In other words, the resources of an area, whether they be food, water, living space, breeding sites, hibernation sites, hiding places, or any other essential, place an upper limit on population sizes. Competition for resources rapidly reduces the annual baby boom to the number that replaces the breeding stock. For instance, the number of garden spiders sitting in their orb-webs, or the number of garden black ant nests, are much the same every year, despite the seething mass of baby spiders that hatch in May from each female's egg mass, and the dense swarms of winged reproductives that emerge from every ant nest in July and August. Death is the great regulator, adjusting numbers to the carrying capacity of the environment.

Tidy-minded people may perhaps regard large-scale, premature death as a profligate and wasteful way of achieving population regulation. Why not reduce unprofitable investment in the next generation by adjusting birth rates to the carrying capacity of the environment? The simple answer is that all organisms are selfish. Each animal or plant competes with others of the same species for food or space, not for itself, but in order that it may make a larger contribution to the next generation. The object is perpetuation of self, or, more accurately, of the genes, the hereditary factors, that it carries. The only way an organism can increase the proportion of the next generation that carries its genes is to ensure that it, or a close relative, produces as many babies as possible. Massive mortality is an inescapable corollary, but flooding the market increases the chances of some contribution to the next generation.

Why then do some animals have only a few young? Why is the clutch size of blackbirds so much smaller than that of cabbage moths? There are, in broad terms, two ways to maximize contribution to the next generation, depending to some extent on the size and life style of an animal. One is to lay vast numbers of small eggs containing little yolk, and to leave the tiny, newly hatched young to do the best they can. A female's bodily resources go into producing as many young as possible and sheer numbers provide some insurance against total loss. Cabbage moths and the majority of insects do this: the mortality rates of newly hatched young are enormously high, but the chances are that enough will survive to replace the parents. The other approach is for a female to concentrate her bodily resources into a small number of large eggs, each well supplied with yolk, which hatch into relatively large and independent young. Tiny pink *Oonops* spiders, found in houses and gardens, do this: a female lays only two large eggs at a time, although she may lay several batches during the summer. The eggs are large relative to the female, and the babies need fewer moults to reach full size than do those of other spiders. This strategy is often combined with parental care after hatching, so that the young are only turned loose on the world when they are fully independent and their chances of survival are quite good. Pregnant female woodlice develop a false floor to the abdomen forming a brood pouch into which the large-yolked eggs are released and where they are incubated. The eggs eventually hatch into miniature woodlice which, after a few days more, are ready to face life outside the brood pouch. Under these circumstances, for practical reasons, a female lays few rather than many eggs.

When parental care involves provision of food, the number of eggs produced is limited not so much by the physiological capabilities of the female, as by the food-collecting abilities of the parents. If eggs are removed from a bird's nest as fast as they are laid, the female goes on laying. She is physically capable of laying more eggs than the usual clutch, but in the normal course of events only lays as many as will give the number of young that she and her mate can on average feed. Clutch size varies not only between species of birds, but also between individuals. It is an inherited characteristic that has been fixed by natural selection at a level that ensures maximum contribution to the next generation. Swifts usually lay two or three eggs, although occasionally single eggs are laid, and, vary rarely, clutches of four. A brood of one will almost certainly be reared successfully, however bad the summer, but one is the most the parents can contribute each year to the population. Birds that lay four eggs have difficulty in collecting enough food in even the best summers; they may lose one, two or more nestlings. Those that lay two or three eggs are safe: in poor years, more young are raised from broods of two, and in good years, more from broods of three, but their contribution to the next generation is always greater than that of birds that lay only a single egg. It is reasonable, therefore, that the majority of swifts lay either two or three eggs.

Fungus garden

For various reasons, the lawn went without mowing for two or three weeks one autumn, despite warmth, rain and plenty of growth. One morning I discovered that a magnificent olive-tinged, brown toadstool, with a thickly inrolled margin, had erupted from the grass beneath the birch tree. As it expanded, the fleshy cap became depressed in the centre until it was almost funnel-shaped. Over the next few days, several more brown roll-rims (for that is what they are popularly called) materialized, the largest of them 17 centimetres in diameter. They were impressive and photogenic, and I could not bear the idea of mincing them with the mower, so the entire lawn was reprieved. To my amazement, eleven further species of toadstool popped up from the grass, some bulky, others less than a centimetre in diameter. Most were rather fragile and soon collapsed, but the brown roll-rims (*Paxillus involutus*) retained their shape and substance until broken up, apparently by birds. I watched a robin pecking at one, presumably feeding on the beetles, flies and other small creatures that inhabit large fungi.

Toadstools are only a small part of the fungus individuals that bear them, and can be regarded simply as a means of elevating spore-forming organs into the air, so that the microscopic spores are dispersed. Important though they are, they are transient developments. The fungus body, or mycelium, is a network of filamentous hyphae, which ramify extensively through the soil, and sometimes penetrate the tissues of tree roots. If hyphae come into contact with hyphae of a different individual of the same species, they join up to form a special mycelium on which fruiting bodies, or toadstools, form. A mushroom is simply an edible toadstool, and the word has no clearly defined meaning. A toadstool differentiates completely while a tiny, enclosed bud, but then 'grows' in the space of a few hours by absorption of moisture and expansion of the cells making up the dense mycelium of stem and cap. As it expands, any investing layers of protective tissue, known as veils, are ruptured, the remnants often persisting like a broken bag at the base or a ring further up the stem, or as scales and flakes on the upper surface of the cap. The nature of the remains of veils is important for identification of fungi, together with the shape of cap and stem, and the form of the gills, especially in relation to the stem. The spore-bearing tissues are on the underside of the cap, on the spoke-like gills. Ripe spores are released from the gill surfaces, and fall away from the cap under the influence of gravity; they are so light, that once free they are whisked away by the merest puff of breeze. It is obviously essential that gills hang vertically, and as the toadstool expands, any necessary realignments are accomplished by bending of the stem and small gill movements. Spore colour is an important character for identification, and can be determined by making a spore print. The severed cap is placed on a sheet of white paper for at least half an hour, covered with a dish to prevent desiccation, so that ripe spores drop from the gills onto the paper. After drying for a few minutes, the minute spores can be scraped together and their colour becomes apparent. It is often something of a surprise, for they do not always match the gills in colour; some species have white spores, some yellow, others brown, black, pink, purple, blue or red.

Six different sorts of toadstool came up beneath the birch tree and are probably associated with its roots. Many fungi engage in mutually beneficial associations with tree roots, forming mycorrhizae. The fungus derives from the tree some of the carbon compounds manufactured in photosynthesis, but improves the tree's ability to take up mineral salts, including nitrates, from the soil. Apart from the brown roll-rims, troops of deceivers (*Laccaria laccata*), a variably coloured pink, orange or white toadstool with fleshy, widely-spaced gills, came up under the birch, and a number of woolly milkcaps (*Lactarius torminosus*), as white and furry as their name suggests. Out in the open lawn were a further six species, ranging from tiny, fragile, yellow and white toadstools, like diminutive stalked fried eggs, and the slender-stemmed pixie caps of hallucenogenic liberty caps, or 'magic mushrooms' (*Psilocybe semilanceata*), to the stouter, brownish *Hebeloma crustiliniforme*, sometimes called fairy cakes or poison pie, which are slightly slimy to the touch and smell of radishes. The burgeoning of so many different toadstools on my small lawn was a revelation. They were so beautiful: in all colours from nut brown and donkey grey to pinks, yellows and dazzling white; some glossy, others with a matt finish; some small and fragile, others robust and fleshy. And yet, like the tip of an iceberg, they were proof of so much more hidden from view. Beneath the lawn must be a vastly complicated, intertwining network of different sorts of hyphae, all feeding and growing – a communication engineer's nightmare!

Autumn gossamer

On sunny autumn mornings after a cool night, the lawn is checkered with small, gauzy cobwebs, sparkling with pin-points of light, the work of tiny spiders of the family Linyphiidae. Almost all are web-builders, but on a scale commensurate with their size, constructing gossamer sheets spanning the gap between two stones or one leafblade and the next. So small are these webs, constructed of strands so fine, that we are rarely aware of their number, unless every filament is beaded with moisture so that it catches the light. And that is exactly what happens in the heavy dews of October and early November. I have walked across the nearby playing fields towards the low afternoon sun, when I seemed to be wading out into a rippling silver sea.

Linyphiids are the money spiders, some only a millimetre in length, which seem to lower themselves suddenly from the sky on an invisible thread, to dangle confusingly in front of our eyes. There are a host of different species, many with shiny black bodies and red legs, difficult to distinguish from each other, although the heads of males are characteristically ornamented with bizarre lobes and turrets believed to wedge the female's jaws safely open during mating, lest she mistake her mate for food. Although the webs of many species lack sticky threads, they are used, as in other spiders, to entrap prey. The spider waits below her horizontal web, or nearby, ready to run to where a tiny insect wallows, unable to get a firm footing on the mesh; she bites the struggling prey from below, pulls it through the web, wraps it in silk, and eats it at her leisure.

For their size, linyphiids are highly mobile, using their silk-producing abilities as a means of dispersal. They climb to the top of grass-blades and stems, raise high their abdomens, and unfurl a lengthening strand of silk from their spinnerets. The lightest breeze catches and tugs at the thread, and the spider releases its foothold and is wafted away. Some quickly catch on vegetation, and the Lilliputian adventurer scrambles up its drag-line, but others get carried high into the air, where the little spiders become part of the aerial plankton. Some are eaten by birds, but most eventually parachute gently to earth far from their starting point. Numbers seem to reach a peak in October, when there may be nearly four million linyphiids to a hectare of grassland; it is no wonder that their filmy webs transform the landscape.

II

NOVEMBER

Tidying up

The first November job is to take down the Malaise trap now that the insect season is effectively over. The tent-like shape, straddling the flower bed beside the broom and the lilac, is so much a feature of the garden scene in summer that without it the garden looks almost bare and unused, and it always takes some time to adjust to its absence. Yellows and browns predominate as the vegetation dies back, on many days the autumn colours shine with the dankness of rot and rain, and there are signs all around that the biological year is drawing to a close. In 1980, the first week of November was the coldest this century, and standing vegetation collapsed into undignified heaps as the water in its tissues froze. Not every November, however, gets off to such a depressing start. Autumn 1978 was unusually mild with scarcely any frost, and on 23 November 32 different sorts of plant were in flower, including daphne, fennel, *Fuchsia*, African marigold, nicotiana, pansy primula, sage and wallflower. This brave, unseasonal show of colour was abruptly terminated two days later, when it suddenly became very cold, and many plants were damaged by frost.

A gleam of autumn sunshine highlights a drone fly refuelling at a persistent Michaelmas daisy, and illuminates the scatter of windfalls beneath the apple tree, where another hoverfly, *Metasyrphus luniger*, its black abdomen marked with pairs of yellow lunules, feeds at rotten apple pulp. A few flies still buzz around the nearby compost heap, but there is more life in its warm, sheltered depths, where brandlings and other decomposers are working to produce a rich, deep brown mulch which I can use later to revitalize the exhausted soil of vegetable and flower beds. Redpolls flit daintily to and fro, with their soft, gentle chatter, searching the drooping branches of silver birch for any remaining seeds, then moving on to tall, swaying clusters of Michaelmas daisies. Linnets continue to frequent the lilac, although the old flowers seem empty and barren, and the gaunt stalks of teasel appear to blossom, as goldfinches cling acrobatically to the spiky seed-heads.

Although there are few insects around, the light trap still attracts moths on mild nights, including angle shades and the occasional silver Y. Like migrant butterflies, silver Y moths may be held up in gardens by the autumn abundance of nectar. Diverted by food, they miss the opportunity to migrate, are overtaken by winter, and almost certainly succumb to the cold. In the morning, a number of other moths are discovered hiding beneath the egg-boxes in the trap, among them the appropriately named November and winter moths, both rather undistinguished-looking. Only males are attracted to light, the females being wingless, like those of the scarce umber, which has orange-yellow fore wings, and the mottled umber, a very variable moth ranging in colour from brown to yellow or white, marked with crossbands of red-brown, purple or black. The largest moth in the trap is a tawny-brown male feathered thorn (females are much paler), which has stick caterpillars so large, that they are scarcely camouflaged on shrubby cinquefoil, where I have found them feeding. The catch also includes a dark chestnut, whose name refers to the background colour of the fore wings, which are marked to varying extents with paler bands, and a red-line quaker, whose fore wings are a drab puritanical grey, with a reddish line near the margin. After the excitement of trapping in June and July, the November catch seems meagre, and as winter sets in it becomes harder and harder to raise much enthusiasm for setting up the trap.

Although I have little space for more woody plants, I decide to plant a pyracantha to complete a screen of vegetation near the road, and to provide more autumn fruits for birds. Now is a good time of year to plant new trees or shrubs, so that the roots are well-established before next growing season. Over the years, several additions to the garden have been made in autumn: forsythia and daphne for their early flowers, rowan for its berries, Mexican orange blossom for its scented flowers and crisp rosettes of bright green leaves, and rosemary for use as a herb. A sprig of rosemary tucked inside a shoulder of lamb before roasting is, to me, as essential an accompaniment as mint sauce, and an infusion of the leaves makes a sweet-scented, astringent hair rinse, preferable to the medieval custom of brushing the hair with a branch of rosemary as a scalp treatment! Loganberries and a grape vine were moved from another garden, but the vine resented the move, languished a few years, and then died; honeysuckle was planted to clothe a fence, and for its fragrant flowers, a hopeful attraction for large hawk moths; and willow, poplar, elm and oak because they are among the commoner native trees and hence fairly easy to grow. The oak seedlings survived only a few months, but willow, poplar and elm flourish, and only ruthless pollarding and coppicing stops them dominating and shading the garden.

The garden pond

It grieves me that we had to drain the little pond in the front garden, and I sometimes imagine that the smooth newts and common frogs that still visit the garden are bewildered by its absence. Tall shafts of yellow flag shaded the pool, making a cool oasis on the hottest and brightest of summer days. It was a delight to sit on the surrounding wall admiring the pink chalices of water-lilies, and watching for fish lurking beneath the flat leaves. Spiked water millfoil grew in the water, putting up slender stems of tiny flowers, yellow- and black-striped *Helophilus* hoverflies basked on the broad flag leaves, orange-bellied newts swam sinuously in the water, and sometimes a bronzy-green frog crouched like a glistening statue on a mossy stone by the water's edge.

Garden ponds are not only a source of pleasure, they have considerable value for conservation. There are many fewer village and field ponds than there used to be, and those that remain are increasingly polluted with rubbish or by chemical run-off from farmland. The disappearance and spoiling of rural ponds have been major factors in the decline in numbers of the common frog, but this was accelerated by intensive collecting for school biology classes in the 1940s and 1950s, when dissection of the frog was regarded as an essential part of everyone's education. Happily this is no longer the case, but frogs are no longer common, and few children nowadays know the delights of collecting frog spawn in a jam jar and watching it hatch into wriggling, black tadpoles. Ponds suitable for frogs are now rare in the countryside, but garden ponds provide a refuge where they can breed undisturbed in the still water, as long as there are no goldfish to eat the spawn and tadpoles. There are usually damp, sheltered places nearby, such as a rockery, where they can hibernate, returning to the pond in spring. They have to opt out of active life in winter, first because they feed on insects, and secondly because they absorb part of their oxygen requirements through their soft, thin skins, which must therefore remain moist.

Frogs, like newts, are only dependent on water for breeding. The rest of the year, they may be found considerable distances from ponds, although usually in damp and shady places. Five years after draining our pond, I came across a frog on two occasions while clearing leaves and vegetation in late summer. These two individuals – or two sightings of the same individual – vividly illustrate how variable in colour common frogs are. The one that I disturbed in a drift of yellow, fallen birch leaves was as light, bright and golden as the leaves, so that it was only obvious when it moved; but that seen clambering over damp soil in the vegetable patch was the same dull, chocolate-brown as the wet earth. It could have been the same frog on both occasions, because they can change colour to match their background by expanding or contracting pigment in special cells in the skin.

While the major conservation value of garden ponds is undoubtedly as refuges for frogs and newts, an amazing number of other animals colonize them, sometimes with help from their friends. Like most small children, mine fished three-spined sticklebacks from a nearby river, and released them from the confines of a jam jar to the pond. Such introductions are ususally short-lived, but some garden ponds are sufficiently clear, well-aerated, and stocked with suitable food for sticklebacks to survive. Water beetles and aquatic bugs of various sorts quickly appear in ponds, but this is easy to understand since they fly. They seem to move around at night, for they are regularly captured in light traps. It is more difficult for crawling, or fully aquatic animals to colonize new ponds, and yet they quickly do, because they are inadvertently transported by flying animals. Aquatic mites, small leeches, eggs of water snails and of small crustaceans such as water fleas (*Daphnia*), resistant cysts of protozoans, and a variety of other tiny animals are passively air-lifted to a garden pond on the bodies of water beetles and other large insects, or in the mud caked on birds' feet. Many small aquatic animals need only a thin film of water. Though my pond is dry, the overflow shaft remains moist, and the muddy puddle at the bottom harbours a thriving population of tiny flatworms. The walls and covering slab of the overflow shaft are well-populated with woodlice, which often tumble down to the bottom – perhaps as they elude the grasp of the large *Amaurobius* spider that lives there – where they stick in the mud, and so the carnivorous flatworms are assured of regular access to food.

Some years ago, my son and his fishing companion worked off pent-up energies in the close season by digging a large, deep pond – not in my garden! They unexpectedly tapped a natural spring, the pond filled and remains full, but was never intentionally stocked. Now, however, it is a well-established, shady pool, rich with microscopic algae, green with watercress, densely populated with beetles, bugs snails, crustaceans and many other creatures, and is occasionally visited by a pair of mallard who dabble contentedly in its seclusion. A pond such as this rapidly becomes a self-perpetuating entity. As soon as it is colonized by producers, in the form of algae and other green plants, which harness the sun's radiant energy and elaborate organic compounds from simple inorganic materials, and decomposers, which release essential chemical elements from dead plants and animals back into the water for recycling, then the life of the pond can continue more or less indefinitely, with no input from outside other than sunlight. The pond has become an ecosystem, albeit a simple one.

Closing the circle

An ecosystem is a self-contained, self-perpetuating organization, powered by the sun, encompassing a community of plants and animals, their non-living environment, and all the various interactions between them. It is able to acquire energy from outside and transfer it along food chains, and to circulate essential materials, and so must include green plants as producers, and decomposers to recycle nutrients. It need not include any consumers, and it is possible to establish a simple ecosystem, with only producers and decomposers, in an aquarium. In practice, however, it is difficult to achieve the correct balance of production and decomposition, and snails (consumers) may have to be introduced to clean algal bloom from the sides. Any self-maintaining natural system, large or small, can be regarded as an ecosystem, from a forest to the community and non-living environment centred on a single tree, from the ocean to the smallest pond, from planet earth to a garden. Ecosystems as simple as that I have proposed for an aquarium are rare in nature. A garden pond quickly acquires consumers, both herbivores and carnivores, as well as a variety of decomposers, and multiple pathways for energy transfer develop. Furthermore, few ecosystems are completely self-contained, although most could operate equally well if they were. Dead leaves drift into garden ponds in autumn, constituting an input both of nutrients and of bound chemical energy. As the wind ruffles and cools the pond surface, the resulting stirring of the water and dispersing of nutrients amount to an energy subsidy. Conversely, when you clear blanket weed from a pond, or when a water beetle flies away, or a visiting heron eats a goldfish, energy and nutrients are removed from the ecosystem.

Can we regard gardens as ecosystems? They certainly contain abundant and diverse producers, and can develop rich communities of consumers and decomposers, if the gardener permits. The snag to regarding a garden as an ecosystem is that the gardener must be considered as part of it, for without him, or her, there would be no garden. A garden is only maintained by management and a considerable amount of hard work. Although, in theory, the ecosystem operating on my plot of land could maintain itself indefinitely without my help, it would gradually change in character, and soon cease to be a garden. Yet the energy flow in most natural ecosystems, such as forests or lakes, is subsidized by wind, rain or immigration, and gardens receive similar subsidies. Neither the elements, nor the movement of aphids, ladybirds, hoverflies, butterflies, birds or other animals, are under the gardener's control. In addition, however, the energy budget of a garden is drastically affected by gardening activities.

Let us first consider energy subsidies. I have already described many of these in the context of lawns, which can themselves be considered as small ecosystems. Every activity that promotes growth and recycling of nutrients is an energy subsidy, and can be expressed in terms of the Calories required to accomplish the task. When a gardener applies fertilizer to the vegetable patch, or sprays aphids with insecticide, the garden ecosystem receives an energy subsidy equivalent to the energy used in manufacturing, transporting and applying the chemical. Similarly, watering the vegetable patch, making and spreading compost, weeding to reduce competition, felling a tree to increase availability of light, and all the hundred and one tasks that occupy a gardener, add up to a massive energy subsidy. In most cases, the results so amply justify the effort that we are able to take a dividend from our subsidized ecosystem. Every flower I cut for the house, every lettuce we eat, every log we burn in the hearth, represent nutrients and bound chemical energy removed from the system. Indeed, the output expected of a garden is so great, that a subsidy becomes necessary to balance the energy budget and maintain nutrient capital. There is no reason, however, why the subsidy should exceed the dividends. It makes economic sense to operate with as small a subsidy as possible, and if it equals the dividends, the garden plot can be considered as a modified ecosystem, where input equals output. I have laid so much emphasis on allowing decomposition to proceed naturally on the soil and compost heap, on making garden 'rubbish' work for me rather than burning it and losing its energy and nutrients, because I see no point in squandering the profits generated by subsidizing the garden ecosystem. The gardener who burns a large part of each year's production, or carts it off to the local rubbish tip, has no choice but to make good that loss by a massive capital injection of nutrients and the energy needed to recycle them. If he took heed of how his garden works as an ecosystem, and let it work for him, rather than interfering with it, he could manage with a smaller, and less costly, subsidy.

However, some interference with the operation of the garden eco-system is essential to prevent its character changing completely. Un-mown grass ceases to be a lawn, and the community of animals and plants associated with it changes in composition. Weeding and pruning are necessary to prevent domination of my garden by a few tree species. Pond ecosystems receive an input of energy and nutrients from dead leaves, but may be destroyed by too many. The reason is simple: bacteria and other decomposers multiply and flourish on an abundance of dead plant material, and in so doing, use all the oxygen in the water, with the result that fish, shrimps, aquatic insect larvae, and many other animals asphyxiate. It may therefore be necessary to clear dead leaves from a pond if it is to remain well-stocked and attractive.

At the start of this section, I characterized ecosystems by their ability to acquire and transfer energy, yet, as we have seen, the one-way transfer of energy through ecosystems sets a limit on the number of steps in food chains. We cannot increase the input of light energy to an ecosystem, and yet we can use energy subsidies, such as the application of compost or fertilizer, to increase production. We can ensure that growth rate is only limited by the availability of light for photosynthesis, rather than availability of nitrogen or some other nutrient, and that a minimum of the ecosystem's energy flow is used to power the recycling of essential chemical elements. The more chemical energy that is stored in producers, the better chance there is of higher feeding levels being well represented: the more nutrients and energy move through the system, the richer and more diverse the fauna is likely to be. Diversifi-cation of the producer level, i.e. of garden plants, leads to diversification of consumer and decomposer food chains. The surest way of limiting the development of a garden ecosystem, and restricting the diversity of animals, is to maintain what gardeners sometimes call a 'clean' garden. Pathways for energy transfer and nutrient recycling are drastically reduced by excessive weeding and ground clearance, and by destruction of all garden rubbish.

On hearing me talk about my garden, people who have not seen it assume, quite wrongly, that every plant must be chewed and defoliated by insects. Why is it that even in a garden like mine, where insect herbivores are given every encouragement, they seem to make so little impact on the vegetation? One school of thought holds that herbivores are limited in numbers by predators rather than by food, which is always in abundant supply. On the other hand, detailed investigations of what herbivores eat tend to show that they are unexpectedly choosy. Most newly hatched caterpillars, for instance, can cope with only the freshest, softest, most palatable green leaves. This means that available food for those restricted to one or a few plant species may be in extremely short supply, and could be a factor in regulating population size. This raises another question, as to why herbivores are so finicky about their food, because most plants, whether woody perennials or herbaceous annuals, produce each year vast amounts of leaf and stem tissue which eventually dies and is eaten by decomposers. If, however, most production were eaten by consumers while alive, it is highly likely that plants would be unable to produce seeds, putting the species at risk, and also that there would be longterm deleterious effects on the structure and functioning of the ecosystem. It would be disastrous for caterpillars, aphids or spittlebugs to devour or drain a tree, because in the long term they and their progeny need the whole tree. So despite the apparent superabund-ance of plant food, herbivores probably are, like most predators, limited in numbers by the availability of food. A peppered moth caterpillar on a willow tree is dependent on the entire ecosystem of which willow is a part. Regular, total defoliation of willow would interrupt the transfer of energy through decomposer food chains that recycle nutrients back to trees, reduce their ability to photosynthesize, and ultimately make it impossible for them to maintain their woody structure. The develop-ment in mature leaves and stems of chemical compounds and hard structures that deter herbivores is just one aspect of the evolution of relationships between plants and the animals that eat them. In the evolutionary sense, the limited impact of herbivores on their food is an adaptation to preserve the structure of the habitat and ensure the continual operation of the ecosystem.

It is this complicated network of nutrient and energy transfer within ecosystems that makes them so sensitive to pollution, sometimes with unexpected results. I have already explained why I am loath to use poisons of any sort in my garden, whatever the problems with weeds or animal pests. Persistent poisons, unaffected by the metabolic processes of animals and plants, can move unaltered through any of the pathways of nutrient and energy transfer in an ecosystem, accumulating to lethal levels in top predators, and contaminating the soil. Even biodegradable poisons, which are broken down by digestion or decomposition, must be used with caution, lest they break an essential link in a chain of interactions. The garden ecosystem is a complicated, dynamic network, and the functioning of every part of it is influenced in some way, however small, by the presence and activities of the rest. Any interference with its operation is fraught with danger, and will almost certainly create more problems than it was intended to solve.

Garden birds

Most people are aware of common garden birds like robins and blackbirds, and recognize the usual visitors to bird tables, such as starlings and blue tits, but many less familiar birds visit or pass over the average garden from time to time. My garden is neither large nor secluded, yet the total bird list for the last ten years is impressive. Not all are breeding birds or regular visitors for food: some, such as herons, are only seen flying over; others, such as tawny owls, alight on the chimney-pots at night, and are heard rather than seen; and a few, such as a cuckoo, have been visible or audible from my garden, although they did not visit it. There is an element of chance in what birds fly over a garden, but whether they land, and whether, having visited, they stay, depends on availability of food or of nesting sites in an appropriate setting. Gulls, for instance, can be brought down to a large, exposed lawn in cold winters by putting out sprats for them to eat, but they are wary birds, and the most succulent bait would not entice them onto a pocket-sized lawn surrounded by tall buildings or overhanging trees. In the period 1951-58, my father trapped and ringed 55 species in his 1000 square metres of garden only two kilometres from Leicester city centre; many, such as marsh warbler, sedge warbler, grasshopper warbler, nightingale and brambling, were unexpected visitors to a town garden.

Birds can be attracted to a garden by improving it as a habitat, with shrubbery, undergrowth, one or two tall trees, abundant berries and other fruit, a good seed crop, plenty of insects, worms and other invertebrates, a pond and dripping or running water, minimal disturbance especially in the nesting season, and no cats. Warblers are more likely to hunt for insect food in gardens with plenty of cover, and visit running water to drink or bathe. Not every garden has a stream or spring, but a hose-pipe rigged up so that it drips audibly into the pond or a container of some sort, is an irresistible attraction. If seed-heads are left on such plants as sage and teasel, greenfinches, goldfinches and

other seed-eaters will visit them to feed, and a good berry crop on rowan, dog rose and cotoneaster brings mistle thrushes, fieldfares, redwings and other fruit-eaters in winter.

It is fairly easy to provide food for temporary visitors, but provision of
nesting sites is quite another matter, since their suitability depends on
the habitat in general and the availability of food. Tall trees with thick
foliage attract those birds which nest well above the ground, such as
collared doves and woodpigeons, and blackbirds, hedge sparrows and
greenfinches like dense vegetation. One reason that I cannot locate the
nests of many birds that undoubtedly breed in my garden, is that tangles
of shrubs and climbing plants are allowed to grow tall and undisturbed.
The holly trees and privet bushes outside my study window were once
neatly rounded; they, like the box and mock orange in the front garden,
had been meticulously pruned by previous owners. Now they straggle
and expand into shady, impenetrable masses, not only easier on the eye,
but offering greater refuge and security to birds. But I have no
nest-boxes in my garden, for these can attract more blue tits and great
tits into a garden than the available food will support. Population density
of these hole-nesting species is normally limited by the availability of
nesting sites, but they are typically woodland birds that feed their young
on the spring flush of moth caterpillars on oaks and other trees. These
caterpillars occur in gardens, but in small numbers, and there is risk in
encouraging more birds to nest, for they may experience food shortage
and unavoidably high nestling mortality. Beware, however, of putting
out bread and other kitchen scraps in the nesting season. Adult birds
take crumbs of bread and fragments of fat to feed their broods, probably
because they can quickly collect a greater quantity than of insects, but
nestlings choke on the solid indigestible food. Ironically, the precursors
of nest-boxes – Delftware pots with narrow entrance holes – were
provided, first in seventeenth-century Holland, later in eastern England,
as nesting sites for sparrows, whose well-grown nestlings were removed
for eating!

The basis of my garden list is obviously breeding birds. Blackbird,
blue tit, collared dove, greenfinch, hedge sparrow, linnet, robin, song
thrush and woodpigeon have undoubtedly nested, some of them every

PLATE II 24 A patch of dense and varied vegetation, such as this, provides
food and shelter for many insects. It includes marguerite daisies at the front,
sage, rosemary and tarragon, fennel, hollyhocks and *Lavatera*. 25 Cabbages
are inter-planted with black-eyed Susan (*Rudbeckia*), with nicotiana and fennel
behind. This is the same bed as shown in 24, but a month later and viewed
from a slightly different angle. 26 Marguerites and buddleia tend to encroach
on the rockery in mid-summer, but provide abundant food for flower-feeders.
The box around the compost heap has long since disintegrated, and a pit has
been dug instead.

year. The number rises to fourteen if I include the wren that built an unused nest behind the honeysuckle, the mallard which laid an optimistic egg in the strawberry patch, and bullfinch, goldcrest and redpoll, whose behaviour year after year implies breeding although the actual nests have eluded every search. Bullfinches are typically birds of deciduous woodland in Britain, but during the last twenty-five years have spread to other habitats, particularly parks and gardens. I am sure they nest in the dense shrubbery outside my study window, from which I often catch a glimpse of the male's rosy breast or the flash of a dazzlingly white rump patch.

The list rises to thirty-five when I add garden visitors, including those that perch on chimney-pots or on the television aerial. House sparrows nested for many years in the roof nextdoor, and are always about in my garden, noisy and hungry. Swifts and house martins must be included although they never touch down, for they feed constantly in the air above the garden in summer, and must consume many of its insects. There are no nesting holes beneath my roof, and so the swifts really 'belong' to neighbours, as do the house martins, which plaster their nest cups high on house walls. They are pernickety about nesting sites; although they frequently inspect the eaves of my house, they find it unsuitable and after using the neighbouring house for years, they abandoned it when the stuccoed walls were repainted!

Great tits, long-tailed tits, and, less frequently, marsh tits visit at all times of year, and carrion crows, jackdaws and tawny owls have been seen, or heard, in all months on the chimney-pots. Kestrels are often seen hovering overhead, and I spotted one perching on our chimney. Chaffinch, chiffchaff and willow warbler are summer visitors. Goldfinches are more frequent in the summer months, and coal tits and starlings in winter, although all visit throughout the year. Mistle thrushes pass through the garden, usually in late summer, and fieldfares and redwings are winter visitors. Lesser spotted woodpeckers are occasionally seen flying around in September, and, although only recorded once, the red-legged partridge counts as a visitor.

If, however, I include all birds seen from the garden, not just the regulars such as swifts and house martins, but also those passing overhead and occasional visitors to neighbouring gardens, the list is boosted to 53. Some of these, such as racing pigeons and three different species of parrots, have perhaps only tenuous claims for inclusion! Many common birds pass over the garden in their foraging, roosting or dispersal movements, but have no reason to land, and most are not

PLATE 12   **27** Irregular, pale blisters on holly leaves are caused by the feeding activities of holly leaf-miners, the larvae of small, black flies (see p. 37).

28 Several brown roll-rims (*Paxillus involutus*) erupted from the grass beneath the birch tree one autumn, the largest of them 17cm in diameter (see p. 171).

usually associated with gardens: black-headed gull, common gull, green woodpecker, heron, jay, lapwing, magpie, pied wagtail, rook and swallow. Others, such as grey wagtail and skylark are obviously on migration. A cuckoo and a treecreeper just happened to touch down in neighbouring properties on their wanderings, rather than here.

Exactly which birds visit or can be seen from a garden depend on its locality. However thoughtfully designed for birds, a garden can only attract those already in the vicinity. Country gardens are more likely to have rooks, magpies, jays and woodpeckers, especially if they are large and well-wooded; ducks and waders will regularly be seen from gardens near large bodies of water; and gardens on the migration route along the east coast of England may have all sorts of unusual and rare visitors in spring and autumn, especially if food and water are available. Nevertheless, as I hope I have shown, even a medium-sized, unremarkable suburban garden on a busy road, in the centre of England, can provide plenty of birds to watch.

Gardens and conservation

I had thought of calling this section 'gardens as nature reserves' or something similar, but it might imply necessity to plan and manage a garden in an atypical way, and that would be misleading. Indeed, I get rather annoyed with people who, having heard me talk of abundant and varied animal life, assume that my plot is an unmanaged wilderness, where nothing grows but weeds. In so many books, articles, and radio and television programmes about 'wildlife gardening' – a strange concept if you think about it! – great emphasis is placed on simulating a natural habitat, usually by doing very little. The belief is widespread that, in the interests of conservation, a garden should be an undisturbed, neglected wilderness, or a microcosm of the countryside. Many people find this view appealing, although it is unclear whether the appeal really lies in conservation of wildlife, or in a reduction in gardening and preference for more rural surroundings. My garden is a garden as most people understand the word. It has a lawn, colourful flower beds, productive vegetable patches, fruit bushes, flowering shrubs, attractive trees, and neat paths. In terms of land use, it does not differ significantly from other suburban gardens. Yet it abounds with interesting animals, including so many rare species, that were it a natural area, a strong case could be made for declaring it a Site of Special Scientific Interest, known in the conservation business as an SSSI. Its fauna includes locally scarce species characteristic of deciduous or coniferous woodland, or of marshland, species which had not previously been recorded in the British Isles, and others that are new to science.

Gardens in England and Wales occupy a greater area than is devoted to national nature reserves, and with increasing leisure time, more and more people are prepared to devote time and money to cultivating a private plot of land. Over the centuries, we have constantly modified and changed the landscape around us, yet our flora and fauna has adjusted to changing land use. Monotonous farming landscapes are certainly a change for the worse as far as wildlife is concerned, but the same cannot be said of gardens, which are assuming a new significance as refuges for animals displaced from the countryside. Man-made and intensively-managed they may be, but they form a bountiful and varied habitat, and are neither dull nor barren. Ordinary gardens harbour a multitude of different animals, and can be regarded simply as the most recent chapter in man's fashioning of the English landscape.

Changing land use over the centuries has produced changes in the fauna of our crowded island. The 'taming' and populating of the land has inevitably meant losses. Some, such as wolves and bears, would be hard to accommodate now, and I am not aware of any lobby for their re-introduction. Other animals whose disappearance or reduction in numbers cause concern, such as large blue butterflies and otters, are parts of whole ecosystems that are threatened, and it is doubtful whether we can preserve such threatened species without conserving the habitats and communities of which they are a part. The garden habitat offers nothing for evocative animals such as these, yet does provide opportunities for some quite large and attractive mammals and birds. Foxes have adapted with striking success to urban life, without any special provision being made for them, and the spread and increase in numbers of collared doves has happened astonishingly quickly. The main value of suburban gardens as refuges is for insects and birds, and it is probably relevant that both can fly and so have no difficulty visiting or colonizing new areas.

Although it is unnecessary to create a 'wilderness garden' in the interests of conservation, much can be done to enhance gardens as refuges for animals. The important point is that this can be done within the context of a typical garden, maintained for the usual aesthetic, recreational and economic reasons that most people want a garden. Rather than a *laissez faire* attitude, this may entail more thoughtful management, but I have been able to improve my garden for wildlife and yet retain its function as a garden. Various gardening practices are involved: growing some native trees and shrubs; cultivating plants that provide flowers for nectar-feeders, or seeds and berries for birds; maintaining good ground cover; leaving a few dense tangles of shrubbery and undergrowth undisturbed; allowing natural decomposition of dead vegetation, as far as possible *in situ*, otherwise on a compost heap; eschewing the use of poisons; and providing as great a variety of vegetation and habitat as space allows. The long-standing English passion for gardening will be the salvation of our wildlife in areas of high population. If any change is called for, it is towards increased understanding and awareness of how the garden ecosystem operates, so that suburbia is enhanced as a refuge for wildlife. Gardens could well be England's largest nature reserve.

Outdoor housework

There are plenty of jobs in the garden whenever I feel energetic, although most involve the sort of uninspiring sorting out, tidying and sweeping that I regard as 'outdoor housework'. I make a start on cutting down the brittle dead stems of goldenrod and other herbaceous perennials and, as the pile of dead vegetation accumulates, marvel again at the productivity of the garden. Dingy, fat caterpillars of lesser yellow underwings are uprooted with spent foxgloves, encroaching marguerites and sprawling spotted dead-nettle, and a torpid smooth newt is disturbed from its hiding place beneath a clump of dead grass.

Roses need pruning, and buddleia can be cut back hard to promote vigorous growth next year. Cutting out the old fruiting stems of bramble is a more painful job: every stiff dead stem seems inextricably interlocked with pliant green shoots, all of them apparently designed to deliver vicious, prickly whip-lashes about my face and neck just as I think I have them under control. There are still a few blackberries on the thorny tangle, but I heed a childhood warning that the devil gets into blackberries once the frost has touched them. They may make poor eating once softened by frost, but I find it hard to believe they could do much harm. By contrast with brambles, loganberries' dense fur of prickles seems benign, and training the tender new stems up the fence is a satisfying task. In some autumns, new canes bear raspberries, never more than one or two, but they seem extraordinarily sweet and succulent, perhaps because it is such an unseasonal treat.

DECEMBER
Taking stock

The dark holly trees outside the study window are enlivened by clusters of waxy, red berries, but it will be touch and go whether blackbirds eat them all before Christmas. I usually manage to find a few berried sprays on Christmas Eve to make festive decorations, because the birds overlook berries on sheltered branches near the ground, but the prize clusters at the top of the trees have always gone. I decide to thwart the birds this year by enclosing a couple of dozen sprays in bags of fine netting left over from making a Malaise trap. It looks a trifle odd, and will no doubt puzzle and amuse passers-by, but should safeguard the berries. Holly is one of the trees that bear male and female flowers on different plants, pollination being effected by tiny, nectar-feeding insects. Planting a single holly tree in a garden is always a gamble, there being only a 50:50 chance that it will bear berries. It is perhaps fortunate, for me and the birds, that three of my trees are female and hence produce fruit, and that the fourth is male and can supply pollen for fertilization.

On Twelfth Night, desiccated holly garlands and the tinder-dry Christmas tree will be the foundation of a bonfire on which thorny garden rubbish unsuitable for composting can be burnt. In the meantime there is not much to do in the garden, and indeed little is happening. On most December days, the only insects to be seen are slender flies, rather like small daddy-long-legs. They are sometimes called winter gnats because of the way swarms dance in the still afternoon air on cold winter days. In mild years, a lone *Vespula* wasp may be surprised at the soggy remains of windfall apples, and sleepy 7-spot ladybirds crawl from their hiding places in vegetation, as though unsure whether they should be settling down for the winter or not. On Christmas Day 1974, said to be the mildest since 1940, a dozen plants were in flower, some, like marguerites and roses, left over from summer, others, such as daphne and wallflowers, anticipating spring.

In cold years, there are few insects and no flowers to be seen, but we can always watch birds, and the colder it is, the more conspicuous and easier to attract they become. Generous householders, prepared to go to the expense and trouble of providing an assortment of seeds, lumps of fat, peanuts, and coconut halves, as well as kitchen scraps and bones, are assured of plenty of activity at their bird tables and the occasional rare or unusual visitor. I envy people who are visited by nuthatches or siskins, and I live in hopes of attracting them to mesh bags of peanuts, although neither bird is common in this area. Siskins are winter visitors, and, although in most years flocks are reported in Leicestershire, feeding in alder groves, the habit of visiting bird tables in suburban gardens, which is prevalent in southeastern England, does not seem to have spread to the Midlands.

Common and black-headed gulls swoop low over the garden, their white plumage glinting in the low December sun, as they cock an inquisitive eye at kitchen scraps scattered on the lawn. When the ground is frozen, they can find little to eat on farmland, and like the lapwings with which they feed, desert the fields until the thaw sets in. Gulls move closer to habitation, and crowds of them hang around refuse tips, making a living as scavengers, but lapwings displaced from fields by the iron grip of winter, migrate south in great, high-flying flocks. They may be glad to be rid of their attendant gulls, who consort with feeding lapwings in order to rob them of food, harassing them on the ground and in the air until they drop worms they have caught.

Paper work

Now that trapping has finished and the calendar year is almost ended I am eager to make a start on tabulating, summarizing and analyzing the year's records and trapping results. In its own way, this is as exciting as the onset of the trapping season in spring, as a clearer picture builds up of what sort of year it has been and how it compares numerically with previous years. For groups in which I am particularly interested, this involves a considerable amount of clerical work. Every week from 1 April to 31 October, hoverflies have been sorted from the Malaise trap catch, identified to species, and the numbers of each recorded. Now I tabulate the figures by month and for the entire year. A number of simple calculations provide figures which can be used to describe differences between months and between years: number of individuals (N), number of species (S), average number of individuals per species (N/S), number of species represented by only one individual (N1), N1 as a percentage of S, and commonest species as a percentage of N. The information can be analysed in terms of the feeding habits of larvae, the seasonality of common species, and in a variety of other ways.

Not all groups are trapped in sufficient numbers to warrant such detailed analysis, but all identifications and occurrences are recorded. The main repository of garden information is a growing collection of record cards, one card for each species of plant and animal, filed by taxonomic group. File cards for plants carry information about origin, occurrence by year, and the herbivores found eating them. Observations from the garden diary and breeding records are entered on cards for animals, together with numbers caught each year by various trapping methods. Herbivores and plants, predators and prey, and parasites and hosts are cross-referenced, and checking the status in the garden of a particular plant or animal is quick and easy.

When entering the year's accumulated information on record cards, I am constantly reminded of the debt I owe to specialists who have identified particular groups for me. For instance, most of the animals that wander into pitfall traps go to other people for identification. Pitfalls provide a glimpse of a facet of garden life of which we are rarely aware, because we are too tall. I remember how enlightening it was to walk with my ten-year-old son in African rainforests, for he saw things below an adult's line of vision. In a similar way, pitfall traps are a window onto a world that we usually trample unseeingly underfoot. The animals captured are those that normally move around on the ground, whether or not they have wings, and most are nocturnal: centipedes, millipedes, spiders, harvestmen, woodlice and beetles of several different families.

Special baits attract an even narrower spectrum of the garden fauna, but often in great numbers, which brings me to National Fish Skin Week. Entomologists at the British Museum (Natural History) in London wanted to record the status and distribution of blow-flies (Calliphoridae) in Britain. This was not solely an academic exercise. Blow-flies frequent decaying animal matter and excrement, and females lay their eggs on meat and carcasses, or in open wounds and sores on live animals. Finding out where different species occur is important for veterinary and public health work, and is sometimes relevant to forensic medicine in cases where there is suspicion that a murder was committed some distance from where the body was found. In a campaign well publicized on radio, a trial week in 1977, three separate weeks in 1978, and a further week in 1979 were designated as National Fish Skin Weeks. Anyone interested was invited to place rotting carcasses or fish skins in their gardens or window boxes, catch flies attracted to the bait, and send them, either preserved dry or in alcohol, to the British Museum for identification. So, at the beginning of National Fish Skin Week, July 1978, I bought fresh mackerel for a tasty meal, baited a trap with the heads, skins and offal, collected the blow-flies that entered the trap, and sent them to the British Museum. I also sent blow-flies sorted from the 1977 and 1978 Malaise trap catches – the samples were so large, that the offer to send that for 1979, as well, was courteously rejected! I had inadvertently included grey flesh flies (Sarcophagidae) in the samples, and a measure of the helpfulness of other entomologists is that these too were identified for me. The larvae of *Sarcophaga* spp. feed on decaying animal material, and those of other species are found in wasp and bee nests, feeding either on stored food or on the host larvae.

Once all the records have been entered on file cards, and the trapping results tabulated and analysed, there is time to sit back and consider what I have learnt from the year's garden activities. First, I have a better knowledge of the garden fauna, about who lives there, in what numbers, and what they are doing. Secondly, it has become increasingly clear that there is no such thing as a normal year. Species of plants and animals come and go from year to year, and relative abundance of different species varies greatly, so that observations confined to one year could give a totally misleading impression of the composition of the flora and fauna, and of abundance and scarcity. Thirdly, I have a better under-standing of food webs and other interactions in the garden. And finally, I am confirmed in my opinion that gardens are extraordinarily rich, if not unique, habitats, of considerable significance for conservation.

The garden fauna

Ten years' intensive observation, trapping and recording have taught me one thing about the fauna of my garden – there is an awful lot of it, more than I could possibly put names to, without help. Vertebrates are easy to identify, but there are not many different kinds, although birds are conspicuous, mainly because of their size and song. Other groups of animals can only be investigated by special collecting and trapping techniques. Many of these are highly selective, and most that I have used sample only flying insects. Furthermore, I have concentrated on par-ticular groups of insects, that I can identify, or get identified. Conse-quently, my knowledge of the garden fauna is patchy, although there is every reason to suppose that other groups are as varied as those I know in detail. The only soil-dwellers that really impinge on me as a gardener are earthworms; these are abundant, but at most I can recognize half a dozen species. There seem to be slugs or slug damage everywhere, but I have only found four species, and five of snails. Although every nook and cranny shelters woodlice, only four species have been identified, and the many centipedes that tumble into pitfall traps prove to be of two species, together with one species of millipede. (Millipedes differ from centipedes in being vegetarian rather than predatory, and in having two pairs of jointed legs on each body segment rather than one pair.) There are certainly many more species of spiders than the 39 I have names for, as 611 are known for Britain. But even allowing for my underestimate of the numbers of species of worms, spiders, and other groups, there are very few of them compared with insects. The garden belongs to the insects: chewing and sucking leaves and stems, feeding at flowers, scavenging on the soil surface, and eating each other. Not only are there more of them than of any other sorts of animals, there are many more different species.

Flowers are more abundant in gardens than in most natural habitats, and many garden insects avail themselves of this source of food at some stage in their life histories. Butterflies and moths (Lepidoptera) feed on plants as caterpillars and nectar as adults. My garden list of Lepidoptera stands at 323 species of 25 different families, by far the largest being the moth family Noctuidae. The list includes 21 butterflies of five families, 244 of the larger moths known as macro-Lepidoptera, and 58 micro-Lepidoptera, including the brown house moth, whose larvae damage woollen goods, and the garden pebble, whose green caterpillars excavate the hearts of cabbages.

I have identified 91 species of hoverflies, some of them abundant, many of them scarce. Adults are flower-feeders, but the larvae exploit a variety of different food sources. Larvae of the majority of garden hoverflies, in terms of individuals and of species, prey on aphids, but a considerable number feed on decaying organic material or on plants. Malaise trap samples also include three species belonging to another, small family of flies, the Conopidae, which frequent flowers as adults. They look remarkably like solitary wasps or other Hymenoptera, and have curious life histories. Females lay eggs on various species of bees and wasps in flight – no mean feat – and the resulting larvae develop as internal parasites.

The third group of conspicuous flower visitors are bees and wasps.

The garden list stands at 46 species of bees and 40 of wasps. Most are solitary, but the bees include eight species of bumblebees and the honeybee, and there are six social species of Vespidae among the wasps. Bee larvae are fed on flower products, but wasps feed their young with animal food, mostly insects or spiders. In terms of position in food webs, there is little difference between a *Vespula* wasp killing an insect as larval food and a parasitic wasp larva eating a host insect from within. Parasitic wasps consume vast numbers of garden insects. Only selected families have been identified, but the tally to date is 553. This includes 529 ichneumonids, which feed as larvae on or within the larvae of other insects, spiders or spider eggs. They have more in common with predators than parasites, because the host is eventually killed and all but its skin consumed, and so are sometimes called parasitoids. The majority of garden species use hoverfly or lacewing larvae, caterpillars, fly larvae in decaying vegetation, or spiders as hosts, although some parasitize the larvae of sawflies, solitary wasps, gall wasps, plant-feeding beetles, wood-boring insects, or other parasites. They may be small, and to many people unfamiliar, but they seem to me to epitomize the richness of the garden fauna and the complexity of its food webs.

Hoverflies and wasps are carnivorous only as larvae, but other garden insects are predatory all their lives. Adult lacewings are delicate, green or brown insects, with large flimsy wings, crisscrossed with a network of veins, which they hold roof-like over the body when at rest. I have eight species of two families, and often find green lacewings attracted to lighted windows in late summer. Although they have biting mouthparts, they are rarely seen feeding, but their larvae are voracious predators of aphids, which they suck dry with specially modified jaws. The larvae of one of the green lacewings found in the garden decorates itself with the drained skins of its prey, an effective means of camouflage.

There are a variety of sorts of predatory beetles in the garden, some operating at ground level, others amongst vegetation. Adults and larvae of eight of the nine recorded species of ladybirds eat aphids, and in some years they are amongst the most abundant predators of aphids. A whole range of different sorts of beetles are caught in pitfall traps, some of them plant-feeders, others scavengers or carrion-feeders, but the majority predatory as adults and larvae. They include some unusual finds, such as four individuals of a species of weevil previously unrecorded in Leicestershire. Amongst the predators, the families Carabidae and Staphylinidae are represented by eleven and seven species, respectively, some of them extremely abundant. Carabids are known as ground beetles; most are black, often with a metallic sheen, and the hard elytra, or wing cases (formed from the fore wings), are fused. Staphylinids, or rove beetles, usually have short elytra, which do not cover the abdomen, although the functional, hind wings are of normal size. An adequate census of beetles necessitates use of a whole range of collecting techniques over a long period, and I have only skimmed the surface of the garden beetle fauna. To give some idea of what is possible, more than 700 species, a fifth of the British list of beetles, were found in a garden in southeast London between 1926 and 1973.

Examination of these selected groups of insects has shown that many of the garden's inhabitants eat leaves (butterfly and moth caterpillars, some hoverfly larvae, some beetles), feed at flowers (butterflies and moths, hoverflies, conopids, bees and wasps), or consume other insects (social, solitary and parasitic wasps, many hoverfly larvae, lacewings, ladybirds and other beetles). Many others, including ground-dwelling beetles, some hoverfly larvae, blow-flies and flesh flies are carrion-feeders or scavengers. There turn out to be nine species of blow-flies, including common blue-bottles and green-bottles: some, including a scarce species that occasionally parasitizes toads, are generally found in woods; others are grassland species, one of them uncommon; and my garden has provided the most southerly record of a species common in Scotland. Five species of flesh flies, one of them scarce, have been identified. This survey of garden insects indicates the size of the insect community and the complexity of its relationships, but it is by no means exhaustive. As I have indicated, I know relatively little about garden beetles, largely because of the limitations of trapping methods, and, while concentrating on some groups, others have inevitably been neglected. Apart from caterpillars, I have not said much about plant-feeders, but the abundance and diversity of aphids, evident to any gardener, is confirmed by the many predators that they support. In addition, there are many species of sawflies with herbivorous larvae, several species of leaf-mining fly larvae, leaf-eating bugs and beetles, and many others.

Insect groups that have successfully exploited the garden habitat are represented there by an astonishingly high proportion of the species that occur in the British Isles. More than a quarter of one of the largest families of moths, the Noctuidae, and a third or more of the hoverflies, butterflies and bumblebees on the British list occur in my garden. I have recorded six of the seven social wasps (Vespidae), the only absentee being the hornet, which I may add eventually, as it occurs elsewhere in the city. Garden records of parasitic wasps are even more spectacular, because they include additions to the British list. They are difficult to identify, and consequently far less well known than larger insects. Nearly four times as many Ichneumonidae have been recorded for the British Isles as a whole, but at least eight of those found in my garden are new to Britain, and two are believed to be undescribed species. The British list includes 28 species of Serphidae, which are similar in appearance and habits to Ichneumonidae, but the 22 species caught in my garden include five new to Britain. It seems reasonable to make tentative generalizations about the garden fauna, based on the particular groups that I know well. Extrapolating from species lists for these groups, I am confident that, sooner or later, I shall find a third of the British insect fauna in my garden, and probably a similar proportion of other groups, such as spiders. Support for this view comes from a limited survey of the fauna of the garden of Buckingham Palace. Because of its size and seclusion, it can scarcely be described as a typical garden, but it is situated in the heart of London, and is rigorously managed and manicured. Nevertheless, the fauna includes 57 species of spiders and 367 of Lepidoptera, including a small moth previously unrecorded in Britain.

Listing species is only one way of describing the garden fauna. In most groups, a few species are abundant and the majority scarce. For instance, the Malaise trap caught 31,136 hoverflies of 90 species over a ten-year period, but eight species accounted for more than two-thirds of the catch. Similarly, out of 16,979 butterflies of 21 species hand-netted in nine years, 15,400 consisted of only four species. Seventeen hoverfly and four butterfly species are represented in the total catches by single individuals. In other words, you have to catch a great many familiar, everyday hoverflies and butterflies before you come across anything really unusual. The pattern of relative abundance is quite different in the Ichneumonidae. The Malaise trap caught 6,445 individuals of 455 species during 1972 and 1973, but 141 of the species were represented by single individuals. In 1972, the commonest species of ichneumonid made up little more than three per cent of the total ichneumonid sample, whereas the commonest hoverfly formed almost 20 per cent of the total hoverfly catch. Put another way, the average number of individuals per species (N/S) was eight for ichneumonids and 29 for hoverflies. Being rare seems to be part of the way of life of ichneumonids, probably because they have very precise host and habitat requirements, and often occupy high positions in food chains.

No such thing as a normal year

After a year or two of gardening and garden-watching, I thought I knew the flora and fauna of my garden quite well. After ten years I am less certain. Every year, there are arrivals, disappearances, and changes in abundance, so that I am loath to generalize about who lives there and in what numbers. This is particularly true of insects, but also applies to plants that come and go of their own accord. In 1971, colt's-foot was well established in a herbaceous border, its fragile yellow flowers welcome in spring and its large, downy leaves adding variety in summer, but in 1977 it died out. It is an early successional plant, thriving on poor soil where other plants are unable to establish themselves. Maintenance of good soil cover and accumulation of dead plant material probably created conditions in which it could not compete with other vigorous colonists, such as wild strawberry. A single plant of wood avens appeared in 1976. Perhaps inadvisably, I fostered it as an interesting addition to the flora, and by the following year it was all over the garden. It seeds freely, and now has to be rigorously controlled. I found fig-leaved goosefoot and little mouse-ear in 1975, but have not seen them since, whereas garlic mustard, spear thistle and hop first appeared in 1980. Other plants, such as goat's-beard, common mouse-ear and common knotgrass have come and gone intermittently. The flora is always changing, often for no apparent reason, but sometimes in response to changed land use. When I left a small area of lawn unmown for a season, heath groundsel, smooth hawk's-beard, perennial sow-thistle and bugle appeared amongst the grasses, but only smooth hawk's-beard has persisted and established itself elsewhere in the garden. Stinking chamomile, scentless mayweed and redshank, or common persicaria, came up in a new vegetable patch made from a well-established lawn. The newly-turned soil was sandy and lacking in humus, but its texture and fertility quickly improved, and these plants have not reappeared.

The story is similar for insects. Although not common, ruby tiger moths, and silky white female and dark brown male muslin moths were regularly attracted to the mercury vapour lamp in the early 1970s. There have been no ruby tigers since 1975, and no muslin moths since 1976. On the other hand, the first copper underwing, with gleaming copper-coloured hind wings, visited the light in 1978, since when they have been recorded every year in increasing numbers. Arrivals, departures and sporadic appearances are best documented for hoverflies, because the Malaise trap has provided large, unselected samples since 1972. Two species of lesser bulb flies (*Eumerus*) were abundant until 1976, since when they have declined and become rather scarce: 496 were caught in 1975, but only 10 in 1980 and 14 in 1981. Another small black hoverfly, *Cheilosia proxima*, was first caught in 1978, again in 1980, and then in much larger numbers in 1981. *Cheilosia* larvae are herbivorous, but the foodplant of *C.proxima* is not known; it may be that it feeds on a species of plant fairly recently established in the garden or nearby. Other hoverflies have come and gone intermittently. *Chrysotoxum* spp. are large, yellow and black hoverflies with long, black antennae, and bear a striking resemblance to wasps. Their larvae are believed to be predators of aphids, although not a great deal is known about them. In the five years up to and including 1976, 29 individuals of three species were caught, but none was seen for the next three years. In 1980 a single individual was caught, and in 1981, five of two species.

Hoverflies as a group also illustrate the enormous fluctuations in numbers of garden insects from year to year. In 1975, and again in 1978, more than 6,000 were trapped (N), but in 1972 and 1979 less than 1,400, and the worst year was 1981, with a grand total of only 885. The number of species caught (S) also varied from 61 in 1973 to only 37 in 1977. After my first year of trapping, I should have confidently told you that *Platycheirus albimanus* was the commonest garden hoverfly forming almost a fifth of the total catch; that a fifth of the garden species were so scarce as to be represented by single individuals; and that the average number of individuals per species (N/S) was 29. How wrong I should have been. Four other species have ranked as commonest in different years, *P.albimanus* having occupied this position in only five of ten years, and in 1977 *Episyrphus balteatus* formed nearly half the total catch. A third of the species caught in 1976, the drought year, were represented by only one individual, and N/S has varied from 20 in 1981 to over 120 in 1978.

In every year, hoverflies with aphid-feeding larvae have formed the majority of the catch, but their abundance relative to those whose larvae eat other foods has varied considerably. In 1976, for instance, those with herbivorous larvae, such as narcissus flies, lesser bulb flies and *Cheilosia* spp., were common, and in 1973 and 1978, those whose larvae feed on decaying organic matter, such as drone flies and other species of *Eristalis*. As already described, there was a vast influx of hoverflies with aphid-feeding larvae, particularly *Metasyrphus corollae* and *Episyrphus balteatus*, in 1975, 1976 and 1977. Rather unexpectedly, this was compensated for by a decline in numbers of resident *Platycheirus* and *Melanostoma*, so that the relative abundance of aphid-feeders remained about the same. The decline of some resident species was dramatic: *Melanos-*

toma mellinum and *M.scalare*, both small, slim, dark species spotted with yellow, breed in the garden and are usually abundant, but in 1977 only two *M.mellinum* were caught and no *M.scalare*. 1978, however, when there was no large-scale immigration, was a particularly good year for *Platycheirus* and *Melanostoma*. The way in which an increase in numbers of some species was accompanied by a decrease in others suggests that opportunities for aphid-feeders are normally fully exploited.

Garden food webs

Anyone with a general knowledge of natural history can make educated guesses at the links in garden food webs – in other words, who eats what. It is immediately obvious that aphids and caterpillars are among the most important herbivores, so it becomes particularly interesting to know exactly what they eat and who eats them. Considerable headway in identifying garden food chains has been made by rearing all moth caterpillars found in the garden, and all hoverfly larvae found feeding on aphids or hibernating. Not all turned into moths or hoverflies. Instead, they produced ichneumonids, all of which have been identified, so I now have detailed information about two of the most important garden food chains: plant – moth – ichneumonid, and plant – aphid – hoverfly – ichneumonid.

The high plant diversity encouraged by gardeners leads to myriad opportunies for food chains to develop. Some are based on native plants, others on aliens or cultivars. For instance, I have bred different species of ichneumonids from bright-line brown-eye moths feeding on native bittersweet, from double-striped pugs feeding on alien buddleia, and from the hoverfly, *Episyrphus balteatus*, feeding on cabbage aphids on garden brassicas. Three species of ichneumonids have come from *E.balteatus* larvae feeding on cabbage aphids; females of one of these and of two further species were also collected while feeding at honeydew produced by cabbage aphids. Tracing food chains can lead to exciting discoveries. One of the ichneumonids reared from hibernating hoverfly larvae was a new species for the garden, despite the large Malaise trap sample, and another, reared from a garden carpet moth feeding on perennial candytuft, seems to be a hitherto undescribed species. But the most extraordinary story is that of the ichneumonid bred from a magpie moth feeding on flowering currant. Two individuals of this species had been caught previously in the Malaise trap; until then, it had not been recorded in Britain, although known from places as distant as Germany and Japan. The breeding record proves conclusively that it is a resident

garden species, yet its presence can be traced to a shrub introduced from
North America. What clearer evidence could there be that alien plants,
far from making gardens uninteresting, actually enrich their fauna?

The two major food chains I have described fit into complex food
webs. Spittlebugs, whitefly, sawfly larvae, beetles and bugs also eat
plants, and blackbirds, blue tits and other insectivorous birds eat
caterpillars. Social wasps collect caterpillars to feed to their young, and
scavenging *Volucella* larvae eat the excrement of wasp larvae and
sometimes the larvae themselves. Ants lap up aphid honeydew, and
when winged reproductives sail up into the air above the garden in
summer, they become food for black-headed gulls. Adult and larval
ladybirds eat aphids, which are often parasitized by minute chalcid
wasps. Spiders catch ladybird larvae and adult hoverflies and suck them
dry, and hoverflies, adult ladybirds and dispersing spiders are snatched
from aerial plankton by feeding swifts. The permutations and combinations are endless, especially if we extend our tracing of the web to
decomposer food chains. There is still a great deal to learn about exactly
who eats what, but it is clear that garden food webs are extremely
complex.

A unique habitat

I have learnt that my garden has a rich animal fauna, including unusual
or rare species, that it accommodates complex food webs, many of them
based on introduced plants, and that the composition of the fauna
changes from year to year so that there is always something new and
interesting. Much of the fauna is characteristic of gardens, but some
species are normally associated with woodland, others with more open
places. The same is true of gardens in general. They are unique amongst
man-made habitats in supporting such abundance and variety. Why do
they develop such rich communities?

The answer lies in the nature of gardening. A neglected garden
gradually reverts to the vegetation characteristic of its locality, soil type,
altitude and climate. The process of gradual change in the composition
of vegetation to a permanent, clearly defined community, dominated (at
any rate in central England) by a few tree species, is called succession by
plant ecologists, and the end result is known as a climax community.
Gardening, in all its aspects, is the activity of interfering with this natural
succession in the composition of the flora, and preventing the establishment of a climax community.

First, the gardener frequently introduces new shrubs, trees, flowers and vegetables according to his tastes, producing what may be called contrived plant diversity, and secondly, regular working of the soil makes it continually receptive to colonization by native or naturalized species as 'weeds', a form of introduction over which the gardener has no control. This dual process of introduction year after year, is systematically countered by a dual process of elimination. Many of the gardener's introductions cannot maintain themselves and die out after one season. Some, such as African marigolds or lettuces, are replaced annually, but many are not, and the gardener may also decide to remove herbaceous perennials, shrubs or trees as they outgrow the available space or his tastes change. At the same time, plants that have come unbidden into the garden are weeded out and every effort is made, not always successfully, to prevent them becoming established. By these dual processes of introduction and elimination, an active gardener keeps the garden community in a state of flux. Without his interference, plant succession would lead eventually to establishment of the climax community typical of the area. The garden plant community is never allowed to settle down, but is kept in a state of permanent succession. The whims and fancies of a gardener as to what to grow differ from one year to the next, as do the 'weeds', so that there is frequent change in the species composition of the garden flora, but it retains its outstanding characteristic of contrived plant diversity. As a habitat for animals, the garden is thus kept permanently in a varied, bountiful, although far from stable state, providing a variety of resources, particularly for opportunist feeders.

Contrived plant diversity is one important feature of the garden habitat; another is the extraordinary structural complexity that most gardeners create. A typical garden that incorporates flower beds, vege-table patches, some shrubs, a hedge, a tree or two, a lawn, paths and other paved areas, is an intricate three-dimensional mosaic of surfaces exposed to the sun and wind, and of shelter. It provides a varied and patchy environment which changes in character every few metres. There are edges everywhere, between lawn and herbaceous border, shrubbery and path, rockery and pond, and so on. The zone of overlap between two sorts of habitat incorporates elements of both, and so is usually richer in animal species than either. Gardens in general are like vastly extended woodland edge, where the shelter and shade of the trees gives way to sunny, open spaces, and consequently accommodate a multitude of different animals, which may be extraordinarily localized in their occurrence and feeding activity. Some clumps of spotted dead-nettle in my garden support angle shades caterpillars in all months and from year to year, whereas others, even those nearby, seem never to shelter any. This may be related to light, shade or some other variant in micro-climate, or it may represent variations in plant biochemistry which make individual plants more acceptable than others to egg-laying females, or more palatable to caterpillars. Whatever the reason, it illustrates the extreme patchiness of the garden habitat.

The key to understanding the richness of garden communities is appreciation of the nature of gardening. It diversifies the flora and the structure of the habitat, offering to animals a vast range of possibilites for living and exploiting the environment in different ways, but above all it creates instability. It produces a bountiful habitat, but one that is continually receptive to invasion. Some immigrants stay for only a short time, but as they move on their places are taken by others. The gardens of suburbia support an enormous mobile community of insects, many of them flower-feeders, which drift around, exploiting food and other resources wherever they find them. They are also a refuge for insects and other animals displaced from the countryside. The garden habitat is unique because of the wealth of resources it offers, but this depends on the gardener continuing to cultivate the land, understanding the interactions between its plants and animals, and refraining from chemical warfare. I love my garden, and I delight in its animal inhabitants, be they bird, worm or insect. I would not exchange it for a wilderness plot, because it would not be half as interesting. Kipling's words might have been written about wildlife gardens: 'such gardens are not made by singing "Oh, how beautiful!" and sitting in the shade'.

With the year at an end, what now? Another year to look forward to, with the certainty of new plants and ichneumonids, the probabilities of new butterflies, and moths and the possibility of another invasion of hoverflies and ladybirds. In the meantime, I must do some sewing repairs to the Malaise trap, get the lawn-mower blades sharpened, order some seeds, scrub the seed boxes, replace the pitfall traps, check the wiring of the light trap, clean up the gardening tools, mend the fence, clear the vegetable patch, spread the compost . . . and start a new garden diary!

Index